WHAT TO READ IN THE RAIN

2013

WHAT TO | READ IN | THE RAIN

AN ANTHOLOGY OF WRITING FROM 826 SEATTLE
BY FAMOUS AND NOT-YET-FAMOUS ADULT AND YOUNG WRITERS

8 2 6
SEATTLE

826 Seattle
8414 Greenwood Ave. N.
Seattle, Washington, 98103, USA, Earth, Sol, Via Lactea
www.826seattle.org
206-725-2625

ISBN 978-0-9779832-5-4

Editor: Bill Thorness
Designer: Tony Ong
Printer: Thomson-Shore, Dexter, Michigan

Special thanks to Sappi Fine Paper Company, which provided a major grant for production of this book:

"We are very proud to support such a thoughtful and creative book. From the interesting design to the unique delivery, What to Read in the Rain *is a testament to Sappi's Ideas That Matter program and we hope it will inspire future 826Seattle students to continue writing and bring works like these to light."*

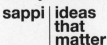

Special thanks to Amazon.com for helping fund this project.

ALSO BY 826 SEATTLE

At 14,411 feet, Mt. Rainier is the highest mountain in Washington State and is an active volcano. This mountain has generated many, many stories.

TABLE OF CONTENTS

Photo by Alexa Robbins

TOM ROBBINS is an 826 Seattle Board Member and author of nine novels, including *Fierce Invalids Home from Hot Climates* and *Villa Incognito*.

ADVICE TO ASPIRING WRITERS

- Read! To be a good writer, you, must first be a good reader, more-over, while any number of cookie-cutter drones can crowd around a TV screen, only people who read have a clear sense of themselves as individuals.

- Write! Write everyday without fail, even if it's only for twenty minutes; even if the nation is on red alert, your typing finger has been pinched by a giant land crab, and your grandmother has just fallen out of a third-story window.

- Fall in love with language. If you aren't already tight with language, start taking language out on dates and see if you can't hook up. Remember: *language is not the frosting, it's the cake.*

- Challenge each and every sentence: challenge it for lucidity, accuracy, originality, and cadence (people read with their ears as well as their eyes). If it doesn't meet the challenge, work on it until it does.

- At the end of a writing day, you should feel exhausted. If you're too perky, that's a sign you're writing your story but not sentences.

- It is not enough to describe experience. You must also experience description. Rhythmical language and evocative imagery possess a power of effect that is equal to, and sometimes even greater than, the effect possessed by content.

- Always compare yourself to the best. Even if you never measure up, it can't help but make you better.

- Avoid majoring in creative writing in college. There, you'll be force-fed a lot of rules. Many of them are well-founded, *but* there is only one rule in writing: whatever works, works. The trick is knowing what is working. The best writers seem to know that intuitively. It's actually quite mysterious—and it cannot be taught. It has to be *caught*. You catch it like some tropical disease.

- Never be afraid to make a fool of yourself. The farthest out you can go is frequently the best place to be. (But pushing the envelope has to come naturally, you can't force it.)

- Be patient. Stop worrying about getting published and concentrate on getting better. In other words, focus on the work itself and not on what may or may not eventually happen to it.

- Don't talk too much about your work in progress – you'll talk it away. Let your ideas flow from your mind to the page without exposing them to air. Especially hot air.

- Since as a writer you'll be spending a great deal of time alone, you will benefit by learning to appreciate the joys of solitude.

- Writing professionally is work – but it's also *play.* So, above all, have a good time. If you aren't enjoying writing it, you can hardly expect someone else to enjoy reading it. If you don't actually like to write, *love* to write, feel driven and compelled to write, you're better off abandoning literary ambition in favor of a more legitimate career. Trial lawyer, anyone? Cat burglar?

Photo by Susan Doupé

TERI HEIN is the founding Executive Director of 826 Seattle. She was a teacher for many years and is a published author of numerous essays and stories, including her memoir, *Atomic Farmgirl*. In 2011 she traveled to Washington D.C. to accept an award that honors the work of 826 Seattle from First Lady Michelle Obama.

WELCOME TO THE 826 SEATTLE CLUB OR:

HOW YOU AND YOUR TUNA FISH SANDWICH COULD SAVE THE WORLD

At 826 Seattle we are in the business of supporting young people to become successful adults. We do this by teaching young people the essential art and skill of writing. Hundreds of trained volunteers sit shoulder-to-shoulder with young people helping them learn to write better. And, important to mention, all of our work is free of charge to families.

If you write well you can fill out a better job application, write letters to the editor, create compelling college essays, and even entertain people with your novel.

But there is another thing about writing that we are thinking about these days at 826 Seattle. It's about how writing as an activity can spark curiosity, inspire creative problem solving, and grow resourcefulness.

Imagine you've decided to write a little story in which the main character is a tuna fish sandwich. Perhaps anthropomorphizing tuna fish sandwiches is not something you are comfortable with, but this sort of activity happens frequently at 826 Seattle.

In fact, in the past week leading characters in several stories created here at 826 Seattle have included Frank, a large white cross between a tiger and a unicorn, Dorthi the Dust Bunny, and Lob, the Tennis Ball. All, after thoughtful research, are compelling characters that serve to drive their stories forward...albeit a bit tongue in cheek.

Anyway, back to that tuna fish sandwich...

Have you ever started writing about a tuna fish sandwich and then you start to wonder who made the first tuna fish sandwich and the next thing you'll know you've done some research and learned that people only started eating tuna as their protein when the sardine fishery was lousy one year... and then tuna fish got more popular as a food than sardines and then all these countries like the U.S., Mexico, and Russia started fighting over who got to fish for tuna out in the open oceans. Then some folks invented a way of fishing called purse seining which uses a giant net run out in a circle in the water and catches millions of tuna, but unfortunately purse seiners also catch everything else—including dolphins, for example. So people who care about animals—especially super smart animals like dolphins—got upset about purse seining and while they were at it they got upset also that tuna has a really high level of mercury in it. Mercury comes from volcanoes and coal plants and tends to stick around in fish bodies until eaten by humans, when the mercury then goes into the human bodies.

All of a sudden, with all this knowledge it begins to seem like having a tuna fish sandwich as the main character of a story brings with it a whole responsibility that links international trade, environmental science, and health issues, particularly as related to pregnant women (going back to the mercury part).

Is the tuna fish sandwich in your story an important source of protein good guy character or an evil villain who poisons its victims?

Personally I grew up loving tuna sandwiches more than anything, so my tuna fish sandwich main character is a super hero who saves the oceans for all...miraculously sucking the mercury out of all sea animals who display toxic levels, as well as convincing Congress to convert all coal plants to job-producing wind turbine factories.

Your character might be different.

Writing makes you think about things in a different way. It makes you curious about things. And, if given license—which is what we do at 826 Seattle: give license—a little curiosity can go a long way.

We are busy creating curiosity, teaching writing, building skills, teaching research and resourcefulness, and helping young people learn how to solve problems.

SUPPORT CURIOSITY: BUY THIS BOOK! When you buy this book you immediately become part of our team of curiosity builders. One hundred percent of the purchase price supports our work. You also become an official 826 Seattle story spreader. That's the other thing we do. We collect stories from adult authors with giant hearts plus the best writing from our students and we give you (aka, new member of the 826 Seattle team) the opportunity to share these stories with people back in your neighborhood—wherever your neighborhood might be—via this book, *What To Read in the Rain*.

If we share our stories, we will understand each other better. If we understand each other, we might be more likely to take care of each other.

At 826 Seattle by teaching kids essential skills we're helping them learn to take care of themselves in the world and, by creating this mechanism to share stories, we're also inspiring people to take care of each other.

In short: writing + research = skills and curiosity = interesting writing = story sharing = more understanding and capable children = better world.

And maybe a little less mercury...who knows?

So—welcome to our club.

YONASE GELETA is eight and goes to B.F. Day Elementary. He is inspired to write by his daydreams. He likes math and one day plans to be an aeronautical engineer. The most important thing in the world to him is his older brother, Brook.

HOW TO SLEEP
WITH A TRICERATOPS
IN YOUR ROOM

"You are pinned to the paper," I yelled. I was wrestling my brother on a 74-degree summer day, when all of a sudden I tripped over an oval.

"What do you think it is?" I asked my brother.

"I think it's an egg," my brother said.

I told him we should take it home, but he didn't agree with me. "But I could study it and keep it in my collection," I said.

"Fine," he said, "but you are carrying it."

I took it home and put it on a shelf next to a box with bones of Pharaohs of Egypt. Two nights later, I was sleeping when something cold and smooth poked me. I woke up and saw a baby triceratops sitting on my pillow and looking curiously at me. It looked at me and looked at itself. It seemed to be questioning whether I was part of its family or not.

"Hey there, little guy. So, you aren't going to eat me, right? Wait, you are a triceratops so you won't."

I ran to my brother's room and shook him until he woke up.

"What are you doing?" he said.

"There's a baby triceratops in my room," I said.

"You are sleepwalking," he said. And then he slapped me. I rubbed my cheek.

"Ow! I am awake, okay?"

"Oh, sorry. Okay, if there is a triceratops in your room show me it," he said.

I took him to my room and gently picked up the baby triceratops and showed it to my brother.

"So, here you go buddy," I said.

"No, that's impossible! Dinosaurs were extinct ages ago," he said.

"I know, right? I couldn't figure out what happened," I said.

"Let's ask someone."

"No!" I said. "If we tell somebody about the triceratops then they will tell the government to get a reward."

My brother said that we should hide her so that the government didn't find her and take her away. Her life would be in danger and because she was the only one of her kind, if she died then the whole evolution of dinosaurs would be extinct!

But how?

"We should disguise her as a monkey," I exclaimed.

"Good idea. For now, let's go back to bed," said my brother.

"But I don't understand how anyone could sleep with a triceratops in their room!" I said. But, I still tried.

So, we went to sleep. While we were sleeping, I heard a big bang. I got out of bed and went downstairs, and I saw people in black suits with black paint on their eyes. One had blue stripes on his face.

He shouted that I had to give him the triceratops. He locked the doors. I said I wouldn't give her up.

The agent said, "Give us the triceratops and we'll give you your brother back."

I was confused. Just then, I saw my brother lift up his face and realized it was a guy in a mask and a suit. He was actually part of the government. I felt stressed because I didn't know where my brother was, but I didn't want to hand over the triceratops because they had been extinct for millions of years, and if I lost her, I might never get another one. But I had to make sure my brother was safe.

"Okay, Okay," I said. "I'll give you the triceratops, but first I want to see my brother."

"Fine. Then meet me at the government base at 14:00," said the agent, and they all left.

I knew where the government base was because it was really big and my parents always drove by it on the way to my school. I left at 12:00—two hours early—just to be sure. I brought a slingshot, a bow staff, nunchuks, a sai, and a toy car that I was hoping the agents would step on and slip.

I walked toward the base. The agent was outside waiting.

"Brook," I yelled to my brother. "Where are you?"

The agent stepped to the side. My brother was behind him, tied to a chair. I saw a small scar running below his left eye down to the top of his cheek, which he had gotten from a knife when he was little and looking through a drawer in the kitchen, so I knew it was really him.

I showed the agent the triceratops. "Okay," I said. "Now, my brother."

Just then, the agent grabbed the triceratops and grabbed me, and tied me up too. "Why would you trust us?" the agent said, laughing at me with his friends. "We're not the government! We're evil scientists! Now we're going to take the triceratops and make more of them and use them for bad stuff!"

"You really shouldn't have told me that," I said. "If, and *when*, I escape, I'll tell that to the police."

"You won't," said the agent. "We will keep you somewhere where no one in the world has gotten free from."

Behind the agent, I could see one of his friends with a sharp object he was going to use to cut the triceratops in half for their experiments. But just as they were about to slice him, the triceratops jumped out of the way over to Brook and me. He put his horns in the chain links that had tied us up and pulled hard. The chain broke, and we were free!

All three of us ran away! The agents started chasing after us. They almost had us, when I slipped the toy car to the triceratops. He shoved it in their direction, and they all fell down. Brook and I used my bow staff and nunchuks against the agents. Soon they were all in a pile.

We called the *real* government and anonymously reported what had happened.

"Go outside your building," I said, "and you'll see something you'd like to see." The government agents had been looking for them for a long time.

Brook and the triceratops and I all went back home. We were all bruised and tired. I laid down on my bed.

"*Now* I know how you would sleep with a triceratops in your room," I said. I slept for seven hours straight.

Photo by Laura Damela

CHELSEA CAIN is the author of the bestselling Archie Sheridan/Gretchen Lowell thriller series. Her books have been published in more than thirty languages, recommended on "The Today Show," have appeared in episodes of HBO's "True Blood," and have been named among Stephen King's top ten favorite books of the year. NPR included *Heartsick* in their list of the top 100 thrillers ever written and FX is currently adapting the entire series for television. Chelsea lives in Portland, Oregon.

FOR YOUR SAFETY

Greetings! Welcome to the Pacific Northwest. As you probably noticed on your way to the hotel, this is a pretty spectacular region. (If it was raining, come back in August when the cloud cover has lifted enough for you to see what I'm talking about. Seriously, there are mountains on the horizon. We hear about them all the time.) Most likely you already know a bit about the area. If not, I'm sure that you can find an interesting array of reading material about local restaurants and attractions fanned out neatly on the desk in your hotel room. But there is more going on here than coffee, locally sourced cuisine, rock bands, multinational software companies and epidemic levels of vitamin D deficiency. Please take a minute to go over the following items that may come up during your stay.

SERIAL KILLERS I don't mean to alarm you. Your hotel is perfectly safe. It is run by decent, security-minded people. Any place with a classy anthology like this in the room is going to have quality down pillows, really nice conditioner, and excellent locks on the doors. I am certain that a housekeeper has already checked under your bed. Also, no offense, but serial killers, studies tell us, prefer to kill locals rather than tourists. (I think this is because you tend to stay away from dive bars.) See. You are not in any danger. Still, you should know that the Pacific Northwest has produced an impressive array of psychopaths. For a while, when Ted Bundy was active in Seattle in the early seventies, we were losing a female college student with long dark hair parted down the middle at an average of one per month. Then, there was the Green River Killer. I was ten when they found the first three victims of the Green River Killer. I was thirty when they finally caught him. His name was Gary Ridgway and he pled guilty to murdering forty-eight women, making him the most prolific serial killer in U.S. history. Heard of him? Unless you're a local, you probably haven't. He has a really bad publicist. And then there were the Hillside Stranglers, one of whom worked at the store in Bellingham, Washington, where I bought my back-to-school clothes every year. Up in Vancouver, B.C., a pig farmer was convicted of killing six women. But they're pretty confident that the real number is closer to forty-nine. Being a pig farmer provided an excellent way to dispose of bodies, if you know what I mean. And that's just the tip of the iceberg. But do not fret! There are some simple precautions you can take to avoid these local predators.

1   Do not engage in prostitution.
2   Avoid being a Caucasian.
3   Avoid being a female.
4   Avoid being between twenty and forty years old.
5   Stay out of vans.

NATURAL DISASTERS YOU MAY ENCOUNTER DURING YOUR STAY

EARTHQUAKES The Pacific Northwest sits on the Cascadia Subduction Zone, a fault that runs parallel to the Pacific coast of North America, from northern California to Vancouver Island. You've heard of the "big one" that they're expecting in California? Well they call this the "bigger one," and it's basically expected any minute. No worries! You're staying at a hotel. Someone has already thought about this for you. There is a little map on the back of your door showing the path you should take out of the building. Plus, you've got fire extinguishers at your disposal. Why I bet there's even a generator. Just be sure to go over a reunion plan with your family and remember, "Drop, cover, hold on."

TSUNAMIS If you're staying at the Pacific coast you will want to take a brief gander at the best route to high ground. Just look for the signs with the picture of a cute little tsunami on them. Also, if you hear what sounds like an air raid siren during any point of your stay, or if you look out and notice that the ocean seems to have "gone away," this would be a very good time to run like hell. The nice people at your hotel can point you in the right direction.

ADDITIONAL MISCELLANEOUS DANGERS THAT MAY CAUSE YOU GRAVE BODILY HARM

SNEAKER WAVES I can't tell you how many tourists we lose to these things, so pay attention. Do not turn your back on the ocean. You know those huge waves you see crashing onto the sand? Every once in a while an even huger wave will crash onto the shore. These are called sneaker waves because they tend to surprise the people they crash down on and pull out to sea and drown. Since people usually turn their backs on the ocean to pose for a picture, this can result in entire wedding parties being sucked into the Pacific in front of horrified wedding photographers. No one wants to see those pictures, so the photographer doesn't get paid. This is bad for the local economy.

KILLER LOGS Sometimes the ocean coughs a log up onto the beach. Kids love to play on these logs. Here's the thing—it just take a few inches of water seeping under that log for it to roll over on top of the child and suddenly it's not so fun anymore. The tide is coming in and your kid is pinned under a log, and once that log is on top of a child, it is very hard to get off. Do not cavort on shoreline timber.

AMATEUR MUSHROOM HUNTING Every year someone goes out into the woods with a few printouts from the Internet, intent on harvesting fungi. If you are a fan of exotic mushrooms, the concierge can direct you to the proper farmer's market. Do not go mushroom hunting. This only leads to poison control getting involved and can make the trip a real bummer for you and your family.

THE HELICOPTER OR SMALL PLANE "LAW OF GENERATIONS"

Occasionally visitors will hire a small plane or helicopter to take them on a scenic tour. By all means, enjoy the view. Just be aware of the helicopter or small plane "law of generations," which states that the chance of crashing increases exponentially along with the number of generations of a family onboard. Never, ever fly with four or more generations. These flights almost always crash.

VITAMIN D DEFICIENCY Due to the lack of sun exposure, we get very little Vitamin D out here, so you will want to take a supplement during your stay. Even if it appears that the sun is out during your visit, the local population is so sun-starved that we tend to soak up all the available benefit.

SUICIDE Your risk of suicide increases every day you stay in the Northwest.* Be aware of changes in mood. If any member of your family starts giving away personal items or writing sad emo songs, you might consider moving your departure date up.

MORE WAYS TREES CAN KILL YOU I've already mentioned the Killer Logs. Trees also kill snowboarders and skiers at an alarming rate—they seem to jump right out in front of them as they're careening down the mountain. It's fair; we've cut a lot of trees down, so they are taking us all out one by one. Still, we don't have to make it easy for them. If you must strap your feet to a board and slide down a mountainside, wear a helmet. Do not approach a tree after a windstorm or ice storm—it might throw a hundred pound branch at you. If a bear attacks you during your visit (more on that in a moment), do not climb a tree. This is a piece of misinformation spread by trees in an effort to make us look foolish. Bears are quite adept at climbing.

BEAR ATTACKS Here's the trick: The proper response depends on what type of bear you are facing.

BLACK BEAR If you see a black bear, and he does not see you, slip quietly away and start constructing a nice story you can tell back home. If he sees you, stay calm and "identify yourself as human." This involves standing up and waving your arms over your head. Do not say the word "bear." (As in, "Please, Bear, do not eat me.") The black bear may associate the word "bear" with food and come trotting over. (People sometimes feed wild bears, calling out, "Here, Bear!" every time they toss them a snack. This has created some confusion for bears, who now believe that the word "bear" means "Dinnertime! Come and get it!")** If identifying yourself doesn't work, try to scare the bear by clapping your hands, looking the bear in the eye, and generally being dickish. This usually does the trick. If not, then make a run for it. Again, do not climb a tree. The bear and the tree will laugh at you, and then the bear will eat you in front of your family.

GRIZZLY BEAR So, basically the opposite of everything I've just said applies here. If you happen to run into a Grizzly during your visit, avoid direct eye contact. Stay very calm and quiet. Identify yourself as human by waving your arms, but do it in a serene fashion and speak only in a low, monotonous voice, sort of like you're trying to get the attention of a snotty server at a high end restaurant filled with elderly diners. If this doesn't work, then curl up into a ball and try to survive the attack. Never run. Never act aggressive. Even if the bear is charging at you, remain still and try to go to your calm place. Grizzlies love to bluff. They will charge right at you, get within a couple of feet, and then lope off chuckling.

RAVINES If one of your traveling companions should vanish while driving in the Northwest, it is almost certain that this person has crashed into a ravine and is trapped in the vehicle out of sight from the road. We are always finding people in cars at the bottom of ravines. Some of these ravines have thirty or forty cars in them, with bodies dating back to the forties. Always check local ravines when you are missing a loved one.

MUDSLIDES Do not enter a stilt house during a rainstorm.

JAPANESE TSUNAMI DEBRIS If you come across tsunami debris while beachcombing, it's probably not radioactive, but just in case, cover your reproductive organs and back away.

OTHER ITEMS OF POTENTIAL INTEREST FOR TRAVELERS

Do not carry an umbrella. Nothing says, "Not from around here," like a person carrying an umbrella in the Northwest. It just isn't done. It rains here all the time. You are going to get wet. Deal with it. We have given up. If you are concerned, do what we do and wear something with a hood.

Cyclists always have the right of way. (They don't really, but they will yell at you if you don't give it to them.)

If it gets above 55 degrees and the sun is out, dress like it's 85. Anything above 54 is shorts weather as far as we're concerned. We don't see the sun that often, and when we do we like to take advantage of it.

Washington State has a lot of speed traps along I-5. Oregon does not.

Almost everyone you meet in Seattle will work at Microsoft. This can be confusing. How can so many people work for one company? Are some of them lying? No. Microsoft just has a really big campus.

Food carts are different here. They're not the taco trucks that pull up at construction sights in other parts of the country. Our food trucks serve crepes and Belgian truffle fries with bone marrow aioli.

The word "beach" can be a bit misleading to out-of-towners. Don't show up at a Northwest beach with a swimsuit and a bottle of Coppertone. Instead think: Polar Fleece. It is always at least ten degrees colder at the beach than wherever you are when you load up the car. You can also count on forty-knot winds and high surf. For much of the year, add sideways rain to that equation. We do not swim in this water. We look at it through the windows of our beach houses.

All the men have facial hair here. No one knows why. They just all grew beards a few years ago. Styles range from the full lumberjack to the waxed mustache. If you have time to grow muttonchops before your next trip, I would recommend it. You will probably get better service at the food carts.

A FINAL THOUGHT Please think twice before you move here. Sometimes when people visit, the next thing we know they have sold everything and have moved here to open a bookstore, start a band, or open a bicycle repair shop. We appreciate your interest and enthusiasm—but we have enough of these things. We also have enough cycle powered smoothie places, pedicabs, and microbreweries. If you must start a business here, I suggest podiatry or opening a nice mustache wax store. If you have only visited in August or September, please be aware that it is totally unlike that here the entire rest of the year.

You're totally going to move here, aren't you?

That's fine. You seem nice. You clearly have excellent taste in hotels and reading material. Just do me a favor, okay? When you go home to pack up the house, tell your friends how dangerous it is here.

Tell them you barely made it out alive.

In the meantime, I hope you find this information useful. Thank you for visiting, and enjoy your stay.

*Perhaps related to the Vitamin D deficiency.
**Do not feed wild bears.

Photo by Henry Chamberlain

Seattle artist **DAVID LASKY** has been writing and drawing comics for more than twenty years. He's created a number of critically acclaimed comic books, including a nine page mini-adaptation of James Joyce's *Ulysses*, eight issues of *Boom Boom Comics*, two issues of the award-nominated *Urban Hipster*, and numerous short comics for anthologies, including *The Best American Comics*. In collaboration with writer Frank Young, he's created two graphic novels: *Oregon Trail: Road to Destiny*, and *The Carter Family: Don't Forget This Song*.

matoaka

WILLIAM DIETRICH has been a science journalist and a university professor, and is the author of fifteen books, including the best-selling Ethan Gage adventure series.

OUR TUMULTUOUS BEAUTY

Looks good out the window, doesn't it? Two mountain ranges gird Seattle. Lake Washington pairs with Puget Sound to pinch the city like a corset. Mount Rainier strikes a calendar pose. There are spring tulip fields in Skagit County, a curling fjord called Hood Canal against the Olympic Mountains, and the San Juan Islands rise like drop cookies from the baking pan of the Salish Sea.

It's glorious, inspiring, and addictive.

Just be aware that when you board a ferry or aim toward the hills, you're traversing one of the most cockamamie geologic smashups in the world. Our operatic scenery is the product of erupting volcanoes, invading ice sheets, ruthless rivers, surging tides, and habitual earthquakes.

Enjoy!

Washington is raw real estate compared to North America as a whole, very prone to falling down, but a long way from settling down. The rocks are melodrama, the next ice age waits in the wings, and one of those post-cards, Mount St. Helens, blew its top as recently as 1980. The Northwest is gorgeous because it's as fresh and unstable as an ingénue in high heels. How it got here is a fascinating story geologists are still deciphering.

Start with the big picture. A mere 200 million years ago the world's continents were welded into one big supercontinent that scientists call Pangaea. Our "solid ground" is made up of continental plates floating on a plastic sea of hot magma called the mantle, like skin on a simmering soup. When Pangaea broke up to send its pieces skittering across the planet's surface, Washington State didn't yet exist, but the forces to create it had been set in motion.

The ancient jigsaw puzzle link of South America and Africa is apparent on any map, showing where the Western Hemisphere broke off from the Eastern. That divorce is still going on as North and South America float west. The Atlantic Ocean grows in width, and the Pacific Ocean shrinks, at about the rate fingernails grow.

Back then, the West Coast was about where Washington's border with Idaho is today. You can drive to the top of Steptoe Butte near Colfax, in the drier eastern half of Washington, and step out on a remnant of that ancient coastline. From its summit the rolling wheat fields are reminiscent of ancient ocean swells. Everything you can see from Seattle today was still deep underwater then.

But as North America's crustal plate sails merrily westward on the hot mantle one to two dozen miles beneath, it collides with Pacific Ocean seafloor—or, more specifically, the Juan de Fuca Plate that is one of a number of plates making up the bottom of that ocean. This titanic collision of land and seafloor shoves up the mountains we see today in two ways. First, as the seafloor dives under the more buoyant continent, its rock is scraped up like a snowplow and heaped up into new chains of mountains that run from Alaska's Mount Denali to Tierra del Fuego. Second, some of this subducted sea floor heats, melts, and rises through cracks in the crust to erupt in new volcanoes like Mount St. Helens and Mount Rainier.

A similar smashup on the other side of the world creates the long chain of mountains and earthquakes that run from the Alps to the Himalayas.

Washington State is not just seafloor scrapings and volcanic lava flows, however. It is an agglomeration of wandering geologic islands that have "docked" with North America after drifting from somewhere out on the Pacific. Other rock has been buried, baked, transformed into new metamorphic rocks like granite, and then bobbed to the top to make vast granite "batholiths" that jut skyward into fanged and horned mountains.

This creates, in the North Cascades, some of the most complicated geology in the world. In Arizona's Grand Canyon the layers of sediment and time are stately and ordered, so a visitor descends from the most recent rock at the top to the oldest at the bottom. This logic can be read like a book.

The Cascade Mountains are more junkyard, pieces having smashed so violently that old rock sits on younger rock, sediments are shoved sideways, and even flipped upside down.

Geologist Scott Babcock of Western Washington University has speculated that part of the northern range may have originated as far away as Australia. Peter Ward of the University of Washington has tracked islands between Vancouver Island and the mainland that floated up from the latitude of Baja, California. The wanderings of crustal bits lead University of British Columbia geologist Bill Matthews to propose that our region might best be called "the united plates of America."

Not only is there a collision between eastern continent and western seafloor, but some rocks are driving north faster than others, so that two halves of a valley that once were adjacent are now separated by more than sixty miles. It's the same sideways dance exhibited by the more famous San Andreas Fault of California, and this constant shuffling produces earthquakes here just as it does there.

Photo by Bill Thorness

The ancestral Cascade Mountains, long since worn away, may have first appeared as a chain of offshore islands rising out of the sea. By about 25 million years ago this early range was roughly in place but salt water still covered the future site of Seattle and points west. Much of eastern Washington was still a shallow bay, filled with sediment that compressed into sedimentary rock and that is today lifted a mile high in parts of the Okanogan Highlands.

Now came one of the greatest lava flows in planetary history. The Columbia Plateau that covers much of eastern Washington and parts of Idaho and Oregon filled that bay with a basalt desert. Great cracks in the earth spewed one hundred thousand square miles of hardened magma, totaling more than a mile in depth, in eruption after eruption.

The process was slow enough that plants and animals could colonize the new lunar landscape between flows. Near Park Lake east of the Cascades, a prehistoric rhinoceros was entombed and left a cast of its body. At nearby Vantage, a swampy hardwood forest left impressions of its trunks.

About 12 million years ago, these titanic outpourings of magma ceased and volcanic activity shifted west to today's Cascades. At the same time, the continued drifting of the North American continent against the Pacific Ocean floor began shoving up the Olympic Mountains and Willapa Hills west of Seattle. Western Washington, like a primordial monster, climbed out of the sea.

The Olympics are primarily basalt first exuded as magma on the ocean floor. The Cascades have some of the same stuff, but also sedimentary rocks from that ancient eastern Washington bay, pockets of limestone and marble forged from the shells of ancient sea creatures, metamorphic granite, and a complicated overlay of volcanic flows and deposits. Rock erupted, sank, eroded, reformed, and twisted.

What we see today varies. In the Cascades south of Mount Rainier, much of the older rock is buried by new volcanic deposits. To the north, ice-age glaciers have scraped most of the newer volcanic rocks away, revealing older, harder rock underneath.

The glaciered volcanoes, such as Rainier, Mount St. Helens, Mount Adams, Glacier Peak, and Mount Baker, are dramatically high because they are relatively young. Their rock is relatively soft, but it has not had enough time yet to be eroded away.

The most famous eruption was the 1980 blowout of the symmetrical Mount Fuji-like cone of St. Helens, erasing more than 1,300 feet of height and leaving a gaping horseshoe-shaped crater slowly being refilled with a dome of extruded magma. As a journalist who helicoptered into the area days after the catastrophe, I can testify to the eruption's unimaginable force—equivalent to five hundred Hiroshima bombs in released energy—and the disorientation to those of us who had camped and hiked in the area. Valleys were filled, lakes misplaced, forests obliterated, and friends killed.

In geologic terms, this was business as usual. Cascade volcanoes continually destroy and rebuild.

The second-most active volcano in Washington is 10,781-foot Mount Baker near Bellingham, with records of eruptions in 1843, 1860, and 1891. Fumarole activity and snowmelt occurred in 1975, followed since by periodic puffs of steam.

Mount Rainier, at 14,411 feet, had a similar pattern of eruptions in the nineteenth century. There were eyewitness reports of venting in 1858, 1870, 1879, 1882, and 1894. It has been quieter since but is considered one of the most dangerous volcanoes in the world because of its size and proximity to Seattle and Tacoma, and the explosive nature of Cascade eruptions. Its cone is half a million years old and highly eroded by glaciers.

Nearby Little Tahoma is an ancestral Mount Rainier that was once taller than the existing mountain, but worn down by time.

Glacier Peak, deep in the Cascade wilderness between Rainier and Baker, is 10,541 feet high and last erupted two to three hundred years ago. Southern Washington's Mount Adams is 12,281 feet high and has not erupted for 1,400 years.

While volcanoes are obvious mountain builders, the entirety of western Washington continues to be shoved upward, with the North Cascades rising about three inches in a typical human lifetime.

This puts us on shaky ground. Earthquakes occur under Seattle almost every day, but fortunately are so small we usually don't feel them. The most recent significant one was in 2001, when a magnitude 6.8 temblor struck. Other quakes big enough to cause significant damage occurred in 1965, 1949, and 1945. A huge quake of unknown intensity occurred in 1872.

The Northwest's "Big One" is an anticipated subduction zone earthquake occurring off the Pacific Coast, similar to the quake that devastated Japan in 2011. The last such shock here occurred on January 26, 1700, before European settlement. The date can be pinpointed because it sent a tsunami wave across the Pacific that was recorded in Japan. Estimated at magnitude 8.7 to 9.2, that earthquake was far bigger than anything that has occurred since, on a par with the biggest earthquakes in global recorded history.

A ferry ride from Seattle to Bremerton takes passengers past bluffs on Bainbridge Island heaved skyward by that earthquake. A forest of trees slid off Mercer Island into Lake Washington, where the trunks are still preserved by cold water. Tsunami waves roiled Puget Sound, leaving sediment deposits that can still be traced today. Geologists have found drowned trees on Washington's ocean coast, and a repeat could produce a tsunami wave there eighty to one hundred feet high.

Fortunately, such disasters occur only once every several centuries. Unfortunately, three centuries have passed since the last one, so in 2010 geologists predicted a 37 percent chance of shaking in excess of magnitude 8.2 in the next fifty years, and a 10 to 15 percent chance of magnitude 9.0 or greater. (Each full digit of magnitude increases an earthquake's energy by ten times.)

Seattleites also sleep knowing that an east-west fault called the Seattle Fault runs under their stadiums and that the Puget Sound basin as a whole is crazed with fault lines. We live with the chance of volcanoes and earthquakes the same way Gulf Coast residents live with hurricanes, Midwesterners with tornadoes, or the Dakotas with blizzards. Life is short, beauty great, and risk acceptable.

Our plastic earth is only part of the explanation of the glorious scenery around Puget Sound, however. The other is abundant water and ice.

About 15,000 years ago during the last ice age, a vast continental ice-age sheet extended across the Canadian border into Washington and finished carving the trench that holds today's Puget Sound. The ice lobe ended about where the state capital of Olympia is located.

When the Puget Sound basin is locked in low-lying marine cloud, a view from an airplane gives an idea of what the region must have looked like then. Only the high Cascades and Olympics poked above an ice sheet that was three thousand feet deep at Seattle, or the depth of more than five Space Needles stacked on top of each other. At the Canadian border, the ice was six thousand feet thick.

This was just the latest glaciation in a series that have carved our scenery over the last one million years. During that period, each cooling has lasted about 100,000 years, interspersed by warm spells of glacial retreat lasting about 10,000 years. We're at the end of such a warming right now. While man-made greenhouse gases may upset the cycle or extend warming longer than it would otherwise occur, the scientific bet is that once our civilization exhausts fossil fuel and carbon is reabsorbed by the planet, the ice will return.

The Ice Age lowered sea level by several hundred feet and bulldozed not just Puget Sound, but hollows such as Lake Washington and north-south ridges in the Seattle-Tacoma region called drumlins. The excavation was prodigious. While the average depth of Chesapeake Bay is just 21 feet, the average depth of Puget Sound is 205 feet, and its main basin off Seattle is 600-feet deep.

The dirt went into the hills that surround Puget Sound. Trees have scabbed over the tumult, but you can see the gravel remains in exposed bluffs above the Sound's beaches.

When the main ice lobe pushed arms of ice up today's river valleys, smaller Cascade glaciers came down those same valleys to meet in the middle. This freeze-up dammed rivers, changed their courses, and created temporary lakes that broke free in great floods.

The most famous flood example is in eastern Washington, where a wall of ice blocked the Columbia River at the present site of Grand Coulee Dam and sent it south in a new channel across the Columbia Plateau. The diverted river carved what is today called Grand Coulee, *coulee* being a French word for "wadi" or "channel." This awesome canyon, now used to hold reservoir water, climaxed at Dry Falls, an ice-age waterfall that dwarfed today's Niagara. Dry Falls State Park gives you an opportunity to camp at the base of this vanished cataract and imagine its thunder.

As the ice sheet melted, huge glacial lakes were created in western Montana, penned by surviving ice. When the ice dams failed, they released five hundred cubic miles of water that rushed across northern Idaho and eastern Washington at freeway speeds, containing ten times the volume of all the rivers in the world. In the Columbia River Gorge, which separates Washington and Oregon, the flood mounded a thousand feet high. It sheared off cliffs, sent icebergs into Oregon's Willamette Valley, and scoured a trench in the ocean's Continental Shelf at the mouth of the Columbia River.

This happened not just once, but up to a hundred times. The lava plateau of eastern Washington was carved into what geologists call the channeled scablands.

Elsewhere the ice was sculpting like a Michelangelo, carving V-shaped river valleys into U-shaped glacial ones, and whittling peaks into pencil-sharp precipices. Water added to the drama, with countless waterfalls and steep streams continuing to erode the Cascades and Olympics into dramatic shape. Landslides and avalanches add to both the havoc and the beauty.

As a visitor travels north, the effect of the ice changes. The rolling gravel hills of Vashon, Bainbridge, and Whidbey islands give way to the rocky humps of the San Juan Islands, where the ice scraped basaltic humps bare.

An ice-age arid climate gradually gave way to today's wet one. The alder and willow that first colonized the glacial debris gave way to the deep and famous forests of titanic conifers that astounded the pioneers. This "ancient" forest is, where glaciers covered the land, only about six thousand years old.

Native Americans were home in this fast-changing environment. They crisscrossed the mountains, canoed the rivers and inland sea, and became increasingly dependent on salmon that recolonized once ice-locked streams.

The rest of us are at home too, in a region with the greatest concentration of glaciers in the Lower 48. It would take several lifetimes to explore all the trails, peaks, waterfalls, reefs, sand spits, and fishing banks left by the geologic drama.

But nothing lasts forever, not even the hills. We gaze on landscapes that seem eternal, but only from the perspective of our brief lifespan. The land and water around Seattle is still very much under construction. If you feel a quiver, try to relax. It's just nature trying to make things prettier.

NY'IL DAMIS-SALAAM wrote this piece as a seventh grader at Madrona K-8 when 826 Seattle came to his class for an in-schools project on poetry and hip-hop. His biggest adventure was when he went hiking to an incredible vista at Diablo Mountain with his mentor. His fondest memory is of his eleventh birthday with his friends crowding around him to witness his eleventh year on the planet. In the future, he will be a poet or a spoken word artist who will catch the attention of world leaders.

MY WALLET CHAIN

My wallet chain is like
An umbrella—you can't rain on
This parade.
The chain's strong, reminding me
Of my never-ending course,
Long, durable, but surprising nonetheless.
The bounce of the chain plays along
To the drumming of my heart,
Staying true all the way.
While I'm walkin' down
The street, the first
Thing you see
Isn't the shining new treads on my feet,
But it's the silver chain on my
Side that cannot
Be beat.
The klink of the chain,
It's like an endless bank of coins of the world's finest ballers,
But the truth is I wouldn't trade my chain for world-class dollars.
Peeps tryin'
To take this as a token while
They don't know I'm a chargin'
My hadoken.*

*A hadoken is a fireball shot from the hands, popularized in the videogame
"Street Fighter."

Photo by Michelle Quint

DAVE EGGERS is the author of eight books, including *A Hologram for the King,* and the founder and editor of independent publishing house McSweeney's. He co-founded the non-profit writing and tutoring center 826 Valencia in San Francisco and sister 826 centers have opened in seven other cities. Dave lives in the San Francisco Bay Area with his wife and two children.

WHO KNOCKS?

When I was a kid in the suburbs of Chicago, during the summer we'd go to Quetico Provincial Park up on the border of Minnesota and Canada. "Provincial" implies that the place was small, but Quetico was, and still is, a million-acre nature preserve—so big you could go days and days without seeing another soul.

We would go on camping trips up there—weeks of canoeing and portaging, spotting bears and moose and deer, sleeping under star-soaked skies. The park was isolated and so pristine that you could actually drink the water straight from the lakes. You'd stick your paddle in, tilt the wide part to the clouds and let the water run into your mouth.

I miss Quetico, but I won't be going back any time soon. Not after what happened to a girl named Frances Brandywine.

This was a few years ago. Frances was seventeen at the time, black-haired and with a reckless nature, determined always to leave the well-trod path, to break new ground and be alone.

Frances was up in Quetico with her family, in a remote part of the park, camped on the shore of one of the deeper lakes—a lonely body of dark water carved millions of years ago by a passing glacier.

One night, after her family went to bed, Frances took the rowboat out, planning to find a quiet spot in the middle of the lake, lay on the bench of the boat, look up at the sky, and maybe write in her journal.

So she left the shore, rowed for about twenty minutes, and when she was satisfied that she was over the lake's deepest spot, she lay down and looked up at the night sky. The stars were very bright, the aurora borealis shimmering like a neon lasso. She was feeling very peaceful.

Then she heard something strange. It was like a knock. *Clop clop*.

She sat up, guessing that the boat had drifted to shore and run aground. But she looked around the boat, and she was still a half mile from shore. She leaned over the side, to see if she'd hit anything. But she saw nothing. No log, no rocks.

She lay back down. She told herself that it could be any number of things—a fish, a turtle, a stick that had drifted under the boat.

She relaxed again, and soon fell into a contented reverie. She had just closed her eyes when she heard another knock. This time it was louder, a crisp *clok clok clok*. Like the sound of someone knocking hard on a wooden door. Except this knocking was coming from the bottom of the boat.

Now she was scared. She leaned over the side again. It had to be an animal. But what kind of animal would knock like that, three quick loud knocks in rapid succession?

Her mouth went dry. She held onto each side of the boat, and now she could only wait to see if it happened again. The silence stretched out. A few minutes passed, and just as she began to think she'd imagined it all, the knocks came again. But this time louder. *Bam bam bam!*

She had to leave. She lunged for the oars. She got them in place and began rowing. The water was very calm, so she should have made quick progress. But after rowing feverishly for minutes, she looked around, and she realized, with cold dread, that she wasn't moving at all. Something was keeping her exactly where she was.

Her mind clawed through options. She thought about leaving the boat, swimming to shore. But she knew the water was so cold that she'd freeze before getting far. And besides, whatever was knocking on the bottom of the boat *was in that water*.

Again she tried rowing. She rowed and rowed, on the verge of tears, but she went nowhere.

She stopped. She was exhausted. Her heavy breathing filled the air. She cried. She sobbed. But soon she calmed herself again, and the boat was silent again. For ten minutes, then twenty. Again she tricked herself into thinking she'd imagined it all.

But just like before, just when she was beginning to get a grip on herself, the knocking came again, this time as loud as a bass drum. *Boom boom boom!* The floorboards of the boat shook with each strike.

Now she made a bad decision. She decided to lower one of the oars into the black water, trying to feel if there was some landmass, even some *creature* she could touch. As soon as the oar broken the water's surface, though, she felt a strong, silent tug at the other end, and the oar was pulled under.

She screamed. She jumped back. And now she had no options. All she could do was sit, and hope, and wait. Wait for the morning to come. Wait for whatever was going to happen to happen.

The knocking went on through the night. Sometimes it was sudden and loud: *bam bam bam!* And sometimes quieter: *tap tap tap.* Every so often it was almost musical: *knock knock kno-ahk.*

She passed the time writing in her notebook, recording each sound, each strike. And it's only because of this notebook that we know what happened that night. Frances can't tell us. She was never seen again.

The boat was found on shore the next day, empty but for the journal. On those pages were her frantic jottings, all written in her distinctive hand.

All but the last page. When it was found, that page was still wet, and on it were four words, looking as if they'd been written quickly, with a muddy finger, perhaps in justification. They said: "I <u>did</u> knock first."

WORKSHOP

PEN PAL TALES

*Stories Inspired by the Correspondence of the 826 Seattle/
University House Pen Pal Club*

Come to after-school tutoring at 826 Seattle on a Tuesday around 5 p.m., and you can sense the anticipation in the air. This is when the members of the 826 Seattle Pen Pal Club convene to read through the snail mail correspondence they exchange every week with their pen pals at the University House Retirement Community in the nearby Wallingford neighborhood. Now in its third year, the Pen Pal Club has been one of the most popular features of the after school tutoring program. The club pairs young 826 writers (ages six to thirteen) with a retired pen pal from University House, and the two exchange letters back and forth each week, forming unlikely friendships and rekindling a love for the mailed written word.

For this summer workshop, the youth members of the Pen Pal Club came to 826 Seattle for a four-day writing workshop in which each student wrote a fictional tale starring their pen pal as the main character. The students started out the workshop combing through their year's worth of correspondence—looking for real details from the pen pal's life to be included in the fictionalized tale.

The results are a mix of historical fiction, imagined biography, and good old-fashioned adventure tales. They are a tribute to the lives of the real-life "characters" the stories feature, and they are a testament to the power of letter writing to inspire the imagination.

MIMI ZEKARYAS is ten and is in the fifth grade at Whittier Elementary. She enjoys listening to hip-hop music, swimming, and going to the beach. One day, she would like to be a famous actor.

ESTHER'S GREAT FIND

Esther was so excited she could barely stay seated on the living room couch waiting for her family to wake up. She thought, I really want to wake them up myself, but they are usually not so happy when they're awake. Esther was excited because of all the presents she was going to receive, all the yummy food she was going to eat, and everybody that would be coming over for the party. In two hours she would be turning thirteen.

Esther was a little nervous because her Aunt Elizabeth would be coming, and she was the meanest, but richest, member of the family. When everyone was gathered around to open the presents, Esther was so surprised when she opened Aunt Elizabeth's present and spotted two train tickets to Washington, D.C.! At first she was surprised that Aunt Elizabeth was letting her bring a friend, but then she saw Aunt Elizabeth smiling. She usually doesn't smile while giving a gift. Suddenly Esther realized that Aunt Elizabeth was going with her, which was why there was an extra train ticket.

The next morning, Esther and Aunt Elizabeth arrived at the train station, and Esther was hungry.

"Aunt Elizabeth, can I have ten cents to buy a sandwich?" Esther asked.

" Okay, fine. You can have a dollar," replied aunt Elizabeth. She had promised Esther's parents that she would take good care of her.

While she was waiting in line for her sandwich, a man grabbed her arm, pulled her aside, and said, "Help me find my bag." He had curly blond hair, icy blue eyes, a fat nose, thin lips, big ears, and he was very thick.

"Uh, no," Esther said.

"I am an FBI agent and it contains important documents. I will reward you with a hundred thousand dollars if you find it."

"What does it look like?" Esther asked.

"It is navy blue, and it has the letters F, B, and I in yellow," the man said.

"When I find the bag, where will I find you?" Esther asked.

"I will be eating and smoking on the bench outside the station."

She went off to look for it. She looked under the tables, behind benches, at the bags that people were holding, and then she spotted it under a pile of backpacks. But then she noticed her train was leaving in ten minutes! She had to find a way to get the bag back to the man! Then, she saw a man getting off his motorbike. She quickly ran to him, asked for a ride, and took off towards the FBI agent.

When she got to him, he was smiling.

"Thank you," he said. He gave her a bag that contained one hundred thousand dollars. After thanking the man, Esther went to go find her aunt. When she found her, she said under her breath, "Who's the rich one now?"

When she got home from Washington, D.C., she told her family the whole story. They were richer than Aunt Elizabeth. They bought a new house and moved to a new life. Esther finally got to take her friend to Washington, D.C.

MUSAAB BARGICHO is nine years old and is in the fourth grade at Adams Elementary School. When he is not busy writing, you can find Musaab playing soccer.

A LADY SCIENTIST AND HER CLOSE CALL IN THE DESERT

When I was twenty-nine and finished with college, I wanted to go to the Arizona desert to study ants. I bought a plane ticket that would take me to Arizona the next week. I felt scared about the trip because the desert has poisonous snakes and lizards. The week seemed to pass quickly while I thought about these dangers.

When I arrived in Arizona, I got two gallons of cold water, hiking gear, a small box of cookies, and ten potato chips to eat along the way. I also took a big stick just in case I found dangerous animals on the trail.

I was nervous as I started out in search of the ants I planned to study, because I had never been hiking by myself before. In the desert, I saw cactus, sand, small plants, rocks, and little streams of water. It was very hot on the trail, even though it was morning.

Before long, I saw a snake. I did not know if it was a poisonous snake or not, and I am afraid of snakes, so I hit it hard with my stick just to be safe. When I killed that snake, a poisonous snake approached me from behind. I did not know it was there until it bit me. When I looked at my leg, I could see I'd been bitten twice by the poisonous snake.

I felt pain in my leg and began to worry that I might die in the hot desert. Suddenly, a big, scary, green lizard crossed the trail and stopped on a rock. Much to my surprise, the lizard began to speak. He told me in an evil-sounding voice that he was sorry that he met me.

The lizard moved quickly and before I knew it, he had snapped away my big stick with his tail. Frightened, I reached for my cell phone and dialed 911, hoping that someone would help me before the lizard or the heat of the sun or the poison in my leg killed me.

I screamed for help, but knew that no one was likely to be nearby out in the desert. I felt so sick from the poison that I fell to the ground. I was there under the hot afternoon sun, then through the cold night. By the next day, as I drifted in and out of consciousness, I worried that no one would come. But help did arrive, and just in time. They found me unconscious on the ground, but still breathing.

As the rescue team revived me, I told them about the talking lizard. They did not believe me and said I must have imagined it because of the snakebites. Just as we were leaving, a loud, evil voice said, "Don't come back to Arizona. You won't be so lucky next time." The rescue team believed me then, and we hurried out of the desert.

I was happy to get home safely to Santa Monica, but sorry not to have found the ants I wanted to study. After a while, much to my surprise, I found an ant in my backpack. It was the very species I had wanted to study. So my journey was a success after all. I studied the ant and wrote my scientific paper.

NATHANAEL DANIEL is six years old and is in the second grade at St. Luke School. He likes to play soccer and the videogame All-Pro Football. One day he would like to go to some exciting places like Wild Waves and The Great Wolf Lodge Water Park.

JIM THE BASEBALL HITTER

Jim picked up the afternoon newspaper when he got home from his sixth-grade class at St. Matthew School. He always read the paper after school with his twin brother, Jack. Jim's favorite part of the paper was the baseball scores.

"Mom! Dad! There's a baseball game on Thursday. The Bruins are playing, and I want to go," he said.

"Me too!" said Jack.

"But we live in Chicago, and we can't run all the way to Wisconsin, or we will die," said his mom.

"Maybe we could walk there?" said Jim. Jim really liked to walk.

"Good idea," said Jim's dad. They packed a picnic of grape jelly sandwiches, Jim's favorite, and they set out on the road.

It took them a while to get there, but finally they did. When they got to Milwaukee, there was just one problem: they didn't have enough money to buy a ticket for everyone in the family.

"Oh man," said Jim, crossing his arms. He was really mad. He started singing a song from the opera *The Magic Flute* to himself to calm down. Opera was his favorite kind of music.

"Let's go to the movies instead," said Jim's dad. "We have enough money for the movies."

"Yay!" said Jack. He liked the movies. He picked the movie *She Done Him Wrong* for them all to see. Jim was a little disappointed they couldn't go to the game, but he tried to have fun. When they were leaving the theater, Jim saw something under a table by the ticket booth.

Let me pick that up, Jim thought to himself. It was seventeen dollars.

"I found money!" Jim said. "Maybe I could use it for the baseball game. Woo hoo." His family came to look at it. They were really, really happy. They all walked quickly to the stadium. The baseball game was about to start.

I wish I could be in the baseball game, Jim thought. They bought their tickets and went in. As they walked to their seats, they heard the national anthem.

"Ohhhh, say can you see? By the dawn's early light." The song was coming from opera singers! The music was beautiful. Opera and baseball in one day? Jim thought. I'm so lucky!

The baseball game started. It was very exciting. Before long, it was the ninth inning and the game was tied. The Bruins had one more chance to score, but all of a sudden Jack said, "Oh no. The star hitter is hurt! I just saw him fall down."

Jim was sad. He wanted the Bruins to win. I know, he thought, I'll volunteer to hit for them. Without telling his family, he went down to the dugout and picked up the bat. Before anyone knew what had happened, the pitcher pitched the ball to Jim. Luckily it was a pretty slow pitch. Jim swung the bat and hit the ball. It went 375 feet!

"Home run," the fans yelled. Jim ran around the bases, laughing. He was so happy. The Bruins won, 16 to 12! After the game, the Bruins' coach invited Jim and his family out for pepperoni pizza before they had to walk back to Chicago.

It was the best day of Jim's life.

AARON ZEKARYAS is eight years old and is in the third grade at Whittier Elementary. His favorite things to do are to play basketball and soccer. He is an aspiring actor.

THE SECRET OF
BENNY GOODMAN

One cloudy day, a little girl was born. As soon as she was born, she started sucking her thumb.

Twelve years later, she still sucked her thumb.

One day her mom came into her room to see if she had cleaned it, and when she opened the door she spotted her daughter sucking her thumb.

"Ann!" said her mom. "You stop sucking your thumb! Or I'm going to put pepper on it while you sleep!"

Her big brothers appeared at her door, laughing. "Dang," said a brother, "she is one sucker! When will she ever stop sucking her thumb?"

"She acts like a two year old," said her other brother.

Ann had always sucked her thumb in her room. But this was the first time her brothers had ever spotted her doing it since she was two.

Dang, thought Ann.

"Anyway!" said her mom. "We're going to a concert. And do you know who's gonna' be playing?"

Ann looked up.

"Benny Goodman!" shouted her mom.

"AHHHH!" screamed Ann.

"Oh, yeah, I forgot. One thing. You may NOT suck your thumb at the concert," said her mom.

"Okay...okay." said Ann. But in her mind, that was sarcastic.

Once they got in the car, Ann felt thirsty.

"I'm thirsty," she said.

"Why don't you suck your thumb?" said her brother.

"Shut it," said Ann.

Finally, they reached the concert. Ann went straight up to the front. But Benny Goodman wasn't there yet. So she went to the bar to get some cider, her favorite drink.

She got the cider and hid in the crowd. She put her thumb in the cider and then sucked on it. She double dipped. And double dipped again. She loved double dipping and not sharing her cider.

"Oh no!" said a voice behind her. "That little creep is still sucking her thumb!"

Ann froze. She recognized the voice. That cranky voice.

"Sorry, Mom..." said Ann.

"I'm getting some pepper from the bar!" said her mom.

"No!" shouted Ann. She put her thumb in her mouth and ran as fast as she could into the crowd.

She bumped into a guy wearing a tuxedo and glasses, holding a clarinet.

Ann froze. She put her thumb behind her back and rubbed it dry with her dress.

"Oh my gosh," said Ann. "You're Benny Goodman, aren't you?"

"Yes I am. Were you just sucking your thumb?"

"Uhhh. No."

"How old are you, young lady?" asked Benny Goodman.

Ann crossed her arms and looked down. "Twelve..." she said.

"Shouldn't you be over sucking your thumb?"

Ann was silent.

"Oh well," said Benny Goodman. "I suck my thumb too!" He smiled and patted her on the shoulder.

Photo by Spike Mafford

NANCY RAWLES is a writer and a teacher. Her books and plays deal with issues of race, gender, and class in American culture. Her third novel, *My Jim,* was chosen by the Seattle Public Library as its 2009 Seattle Reads selection. Nancy enjoys the vigorous debates surrounding public education, and her latest novel, *Miz Sparks Is On Fire And This Ain't No Drill,* explores the challenges of teaching in the public schools.

RIVER OF FIRE

On that day when the cotton was burning and everyone was on fire with fear, my father rose before dawn, drank his coffee with milk, and attended early morning Mass at St. Rose de Lima Church. As gunships made their way up the Mississippi, he brushed the dust from his boots. All the bells of New Orleans wailed in consternation. *The Union has arrived,* they repeated over and over.

By now, there were wagons rumbling through the streets, filled with Confederate soldiers leaving town. The clanking of iron against wood, the firing of guns in the air, the gruff voices of men vowing vengeance—I didn't have to see them to know who was passing. My father had been gone no more than five minutes when a frantic knocking shook our door. My mother signaled for us to be quiet.

The knocking grew louder. I was certain militiamen would burst through the door and ransack our house for money and provisions. Maybe they would set the house on fire with us inside. Two weeks before, they had burned the house of a suspected Union sympathizer. She wasn't home at the time, but the slaves she was hiding had to run for their lives. Seven of them were captured and sold at the market during Holy Week. One young girl got away.

The heat of our shuttered house and the terror in my heart caused sweat to pour down my forehead. My sister Danielle grabbed my hand and squeezed it.

"Open the door," a man's voice shouted.

We could hear him pacing the length of the porch, looking for an opening. We didn't make a move.

"Open the door right now." The voice sounded familiar. Danielle let out a sigh of relief. It was Old Man Renard, who wandered the neighborhood stealing eggs and linens. One evening, my father caught him and promised to turn him over to the police if he ever set foot on our property again. The knocking continued.

"Madame Pierre, I know you're inside. I have seen your husband walking down the street with another woman on his arm."

"You're a liar, Renard, a liar and a thief. Leave my door at once."

"I've come for my chicken, Madame. Please give me your fattest one. I need it for a special offering in this time of war."

"My chickens aren't for sacrificing. They're only for eating."

"Then, that is very good news, indeed, for Renard is very hungry."

"I won't give you a chicken, not even an egg. Go away, or you'll face my wrath."

"A gentle woman like you? To say such things to an innocent beggar like me? Where is Marcel? Marcel will give me a chicken. He loves his Uncle Renard."

The idea that I was related to such a ne'er-do-well made me wish to defend myself against the charge of misplaced affection. But my mother placed her finger over my lips, and I remained quiet. However, Danielle began to pound the door from the inside. Each time Renard knocked, she drummed out an answering knock, two beats to his one. I soon joined her, and there was nothing my mother could do to stop us. No more words passed between us. A shrill whistle sounded, and we could hear him running off.

As soon as he ceased his torment, my mother ordered us into the yard to fetch the chickens. There were five of them, and every day we had at least three eggs. We knew what it was to live on nothing but eggs for weeks at a time. Whenever I brought my mother the eggs I had gathered, she examined each one like a precious jewel before lowering it into the pot. Now, we would have to eat the chickens in order to stay alive.

"Mama, where will we put the chickens?" I asked.

She thought for a moment. "In the armoire," she replied. "Take out all the clothes and bring them to me. We'll pack a valise to keep by the door."

Danielle declared packing to be her job, leaving me as the only one to fetch the birds. Her white frock was far too lovely to risk handling chickens. By contrast, my clothes were in need of repair, especially my blue shorts, which were well acquainted with the bark of our school's magnolia tree. Though my mother was a seamstress, she despaired of my clothing. She refused to patch my shorts, which no amount of stitching could redeem. It was past the time for me to be breeched. If not for the war, I would have been wearing trousers.

In the dusty yard, I knelt on my bare knees and summoned the chickens to me. They were busy pecking and pretended not to see me. They must have sensed something was wrong. I wasn't sitting with my legs crossed and inviting them to perch. My hand was extended with kernels of corn, but still they wouldn't approach me. Finally, the blond one sidled up to me. I stroked her back.

As I reached down to pick her up, I was startled by the sound of a shrill whistle coming from above. I looked up and saw two bare feet dangling from the roof. Before I could rise, they leapt over my head and landed directly in front of me, scattering squawking chickens in every direction.

I recognized the trousers as belonging to a boy named Gustave, the slave of one Mr. Tasse. His patches were plentiful, and it was hard to discern the original dungarees. The stitches that held them together were far apart and crooked. No doubt, this rough boy sewed them himself.

I bent down and covered my head with my hands, afraid Gustave would box my ears, which he had done on more than one occasion. But he stooped down and tapped me gently on the shoulder. "Where is Danielle?" he wanted to know.

"Why have you come?" I met the gaze of his coal black eyes and held it until he blinked.

"I have a message for her." He shifted from side to side.

"Give it to me and I'll give it to her." I squinted at him.

He picked up some dirt and rubbed it between his hands. "The message is for your father," he said, "but first I must see your sister."

"My father is not here. Go home," I said.

"Then I must give it to your mother. Let me see Danielle."

I stood up and looked down upon him. His hair was black and curly like mine, but there the resemblance ended. It seemed as if his hair had never been combed, while mine was as soft as a girl's. How Danielle could have anything to do with this boy was beyond my imaginings. But I had seen her kiss him near the woodpile when she thought no one was looking. And like the henpecked little brother I was, I agreed to say nothing to our parents in exchange for a painted top, carved by this same Gustave.

"Hurry, Marcel," he urged. "Just now, I've seen many boys heading for the docks. They taunted me to come and burn the cotton with them. When I refused, they called me a traitor. It's not safe for me to be out." He grabbed me by the shoulders. "Please," he whispered, "bring Danielle to me before it's too late."

The force of his grip frightened me. At thirteen, Gustave was sturdy and self-possessed. He had run the alleyways, cutting across courtyards and hurtling himself over walls to reach our house. His shirt was torn and his hands were bleeding from cuts to the fingers. I agreed to fetch Danielle in exchange for a lesson in whistling. Gustave waited by the woodpile. The chickens stayed out of his way.

When I went inside, Danielle was trying on my mother's wedding gown, which would one day belong to her. It was too big in the bosom, too wide in the waist, too loose in the hips, and too short in the legs. Still, Danielle looked stunning.

"You'd better take that off before Mama sees you," I warned.

"Mama is packing our papers," she said. "She doesn't wish to be disturbed."

I knew she was telling the truth. Without our papers, we wouldn't be able to prove we were free. Most important were my father's writ of manumission along with the letter from his former master testifying to his upstanding character. Their marriage certificate confirmed they were legally wed and properly blessed by God. The deed to the house showed they owned property, something slaves were not allowed to do. Our school records established us as serious students of the Institution Catholique des Orphelins Indigents, which demanded all our devotion, orphaned or not. Our Bible contained our full names, birth and baptismal dates, along with the names of all the known ancestors stretching back to Haiti, Africa, and Europe.

"Someone is waiting for you by the woodpile," I solemnly proclaimed.

Danielle dropped the veil to the floor. "Why didn't you tell me sooner? How long has he been there?" She started to change right in front of me. "Tell him to carry some wood to the oven for me. Go quickly before Mama hears us. And stop looking at my breasts, little boy."

My face flushed hot as the blood rose to my cheeks. I ran out of the house and over to the woodpile.

"My sister wants you to carry wood to the oven," I ordered the waiting Gustave.

"What? Am I her slave?" He crossed his muscular arms.

"Then why are you waiting by our woodpile when you have no business here?"

He thought a minute. Perhaps I had a point. He would rather be caught working than caught waiting. He lifted a bundle of logs as if they were twigs. A lizard ran out from under them.

I heard my mother calling Danielle.

"I'm almost finished, Mama," she answered. "I'm just going to collect some straw for the armoire. I'll see what became of Marcel."

Mr. Tasse had a son, a pale and sickly young man. His name was Vincent, and he had his eye on Danielle. I supposed if I were she, Gustave might have seemed oddly charming next to someone like Vincent. At least Gustave had a skill or two, and he was as strong as any man. From what I could tell, Vincent was good for nothing, and his father was a drinker and gambler of the worst sort. He was known to lash his slaves with a heavy belt, and Gustave had the scars to prove it. My mother clearly held the old man in esteem for reasons unknown to me. According to her, he had once looked very fine on a horse, but that must have been many years before I was born. Even with ample support from Gustave, I doubted he could mount a horse without falling off or, once astride, keep control of the animal or himself.

Danielle appeared at the backdoor, having changed into her frock in record time. Her eyes lit up at the sight of Gustave. On her way to greet him, she pinched me hard on the back of my arm. I yelled as if she were murdering me. She responded by punching me in the shoulder. Whimpering, I retreated to the back steps.

Danielle and Gustave embraced. He kissed her on both cheeks. She smiled. He whispered in her ear. She blushed. He held her face in his hands. She took his hands in hers and examined the blood on his fingers. He said it was nothing. She offered to bandage them, but he wouldn't hear of it. There was no time to spend nursing small wounds that would heal by the end of the day.

Unfortunately for them, my bloodcurdling protest had attracted my mother. From the look on her face, I could tell she'd been crying.

"What's going on here? Why is that boy in my yard? Danielle? Marcel? Answer me at once." Her eyes were filled with hurt.

Gustave was the first to reply. "Madame Pierre, I bring a message for you from my master."

"Oh, Mama," confessed Danielle. "I asked him to help with the wood."

"What is that blood on your cheek?" My mother was fuming. "Go inside, Danielle. Take the straw and go."

Danielle hurriedly gathered a bundle of straw, careful not to look at Gustave. She disappeared inside.

"What's the message? Out with it." My mother glared at Gustave.

"My master is taking his family to Cane River for safekeeping."

"What's that got to do with me?"

"He says there's room in the coach for you and your children."

"Oh, is there now?"

"He says he'll send the coach around at four."

"Tell him not to bother. I'm staying in the city with my husband."

"The city is no longer safe for women and children." He paused. "Madame, where is your husband now?"

My mother blanched. "What a rude boy, you are. It's not your place to inquire about my husband."

"My master bade me bring this message to Monsieur Pierre." He looked down at his dusty feet. "But he is not here, so I have given it to you, Madame."

"Tell your master Monsieur Pierre has gone to church, as he does every morning. Is there anything else your master would like to know?"

"No, Madame. I'm sorry to disturb you." He stood very still.

"Be off with you." My mother waved him away with the back of her hand.

He didn't move. "Forgive me, Madame, but my master was very firm. He said he wouldn't take no for an answer."

"Go away." My mother's ire was rising.

"Please, Madame. He said he would beat me if I came back with a no."

We knew it was true, as did everyone who knew Mr. Tasse. The only thing worse than listening to an infant cry inconsolably was to hear one of his slaves being beaten. I once had the misfortune to be in the vicinity of his house when Gustave was being lashed. As his voice tried to find its way between courage and pain, his terrible cries filled me with an anguish I have never forgotten. My mother's eyes softened, and she addressed him in a comforting tone.

"We won't let that happen to you. Please tell Mr. Tasse to send the coach to our house this afternoon. I will decide then whether the children will go or stay."

"Thank you, Madame, for your kindness." With that, a crestfallen Gustave departed.

It was only then that I realized Danielle had been standing at the back door listening. She slammed the door and ran inside. My mother quickly followed. I stayed outside a few moments longer. I couldn't believe my ears. My father was the only one who went to Cane River country. His people there were slaves, and it made him sad to see them. Now my mother was talking of sending us away with a man who beat his slaves. The extent of her betrayal made my heart thunder. My tears flowed as violently as a summer storm. Before I entered the house, I splashed my face with water.

Inside I met with the tension of a house at war. Danielle had spilled herself across her bed. She refused to look at my mother.

"How can you send us away?" She was shaking with fury.

"It would just be for a little while, until things are settled here. There would be plenty of food to eat, and you could rest your nerves." My mother tried to reassure her.

"Rest my nerves? How could I do so if Vincent is there, staring at me with his pale eyes? I want nothing to do with the Tasse family," Danielle declared.

"Only with Gustave, no? Danielle, you must listen to me. I made a mess of my life when I married your father. I disobeyed my mother and she never forgave me. Promise me you won't do the same. You must marry a man with money. Then, your children won't have to suffer." She wrung her hands as she said the words.

"You don't know anything about my suffering," Danielle muttered bitterly. "If you did, you wouldn't speak ill of my father. It's not food I need. It's a future. I've no future with Vincent Tasse. Of this, you can be sure." She turned her face to the wall.

My mother reached out to Danielle, but she batted away her hand. For the second time in the space of half an hour, I felt sorry for my sister.

The hurt in my mother's eyes soon turned to anger. "You will do as I say," she said sternly, "both of you." She turned and looked at me.

My mother's world was collapsing, folding in on itself like a delicately embroidered handkerchief. Everything she knew to be right and good—her proper marriage, her house in the city, her growing children—had suddenly become a burden to be weighed and found wanting. It was up to me to find my father and bring him back home so he could set things right again.

I opened the back door just wide enough to let myself out. What I saw next startled me. A bearded, disheveled Renard was pursuing the chickens in a wild dance. The melody was one only he could hear.

"The river, she burns." His eyes were wild with excitement. "Her flames rise higher and higher. Old Mississippi, she burns with cannon fire."

Before I could decide what to do, he grabbed the blond hen and ran off with her.

Editor's note: This is an excerpt from the novel A Palm Branch for My Papa.

KIERA RUDDEN-FLANAGAN defeated Voldemort during her fourth year at Hogwarts—on the Wii! She is twelve years old and attends St. John School (in addition to Hogwarts). This wild tale was written as a part of 826 Seattle's Postcard Adventures workshop.

LONDON ZOO ESCAPE

Once upon a time, a couple named Leo and Lily went on a fabulous vacation to London, England. (I can tell you the story firsthand, since I am one of those two people. My name is Lily.)

One day, we were drinking high tea at the Brasserie Roux Tea Lounge when, out of the blue, a pig with an odd-looking beard ran toward us at a terrifying pace! The pig jumped on the table and started gobbling our fruit.

Leo screamed, "Get away from me! Scram!"

He turned away in fear and saw something even worse in the window.

"AAAHHH! A TIGER!" he screamed. (By the way, in case you haven't realized it, Leo is a scaredy cat.)

What is going on? I thought to myself. *What did we do to deserve this?*

The tiger jumped through the window and over to our table. He had huge, strong-looking legs and thick black stripes on his belly. He came racing up to us and...CHOMP!

A few seconds later, the pig was dead. There was nothing left of it but his bones and unusually big beard. Unfortunately, my plain black shirt was covered in pig's blood that looked greenish.

"Pooh, that shirt was a souvenir from Paris," I muttered under my breath as I looked down at the mess on my chest.

I heard Leo say, "Uh, Lily, you should, um, just, uh, look out."

"Why?" I asked.

"The tiger is... looking... right... at... YOU!" he replied shakily .

"Why didn't you tell me sooner?!?" I yelled.

We started sprinting toward the nearest Tube station and got off at the first stop, which happened to be right by the London Bridge. People looked at us oddly, wondering what was up, so we put our sweatshirts on over our pig-blood-stained t-shirts and started walking across the bridge, acting casual.

We were almost across when, all of a sudden, we heard the quiet padding of the tiger's footsteps behind us. We turned around and saw him slowly walking toward us, his huge leg muscles tense. A double-decker bus had broken down at the end of the bridge and was blocking our way. The only place to go was back the way we'd come, right past where the tiger was. We were stuck.

With no other options, we jumped, screaming, into the Thames River. As we fell, I saw trainers from the London Zoo running toward the unlucky tiger to tie him up.

Leo and I dropped with a splash into the cold depths of the Thames. Luckily, a very nice man named Evan was lollygagging in his boat nearby and rescued us. Evan motored us to shore, and we thanked him and hurried back to our room in London's Tourist Hotel.

Once we got dried off and into clean clothes, Leo said, "Why don't we go to see Platform 9 3/4 at King's Cross Station? You know, where Harry Potter always left for school?"

"Sure!" I replied enthusiastically, and off we went. Luckily, the most dangerous thing at Platform 9 3/4 was a luggage cart someone pushed so hard we had to jump out of the way. Later, when I thought about the day, I felt lucky that we had survived.

Then I remembered that we had forgotten to pay for our tea! And we hadn't finished those delicious scones. One thing's for sure —we're never going back there again. Next time we'll choose a quiet tea shop that is nowhere near any zoo.

Photo by Roseanne Olson

KATHLEEN FLENNIKEN is the 2012-2014 Washington State Poet Laureate. Her books are *Plume*, a meditation on the Hanford Nuclear Site, and *Famous*, named a Notable Book by the American Library Association and a finalist for the Washington State Book Award. Flenniken's awards include a Pushcart Prize and fellowships from the National Endowment for the Arts and Artist Trust.

THREE POEMS

A GREAT PHYSICIST RECALLS
THE MANHATTAN PROJECT
-John A. Wheeler (1911-2008)

Think of our little group with a map spread out in front of us—
great expanses of the empty west—as if we were new Columbuses.

Think of it—a *desert* in Washington State. Along the icy blue Columbia.
Think of the caravan of laborers, several hundred a night, unloading at Pasco.

Immense mess halls accommodating thousands. Big band dances.
Beer joints with ground-level windows for tear gas. Constant construction.
When the chain reaction at B Reactor died that first night,
the mood was excitement and puzzlement. As for whether

I solved the poisoning riddle, let no man be his own judge.
Fermi was there. A marvelous person. One scorching Sunday afternoon,

our group hiked along a rushing irrigation canal. If we jumped in,
how would we get out? Fermi thought our ropes were sissy. The water
dragged him downstream clambering, until he reappeared,
roughed up, shins bleeding. That was Fermi. That's how he got things done.

I recall a Sunday with the children hiking in the Horse Heaven Hills.
I watched my youngest climb as the sun blazed behind her golden hair

and realized that halos were not a painter's invention,
but a consequence of nature. Have you ever held plutonium

in your hand? Someone once gave me a piece shaped and nickel-plated
so alpha particles couldn't reach the skin. It was the temperature, you see,

the element producing heat to keep itself warm—not for ten
or a hundred years, but thousands of years. This is the energy contained

in Hanford's fuel. I think of that place as a song not properly sung.
A romantic song. And not one person in a hundred knows the tune.

RICHLAND DOCK

2006

The Columbia rolls on
through the desert,
unimpressed and unattached—
a woman who doesn't need boys
to dance, a king's parade
of golden carriages,
an endless line of warrior ants.
The river speaks French
in a land of inferior grammar.
The river is blue in a field of brown,
green in a field of gray,
black in a field of bronze.
The river shuns the desert.
It holds its tongue.
It saves itself for the ocean.
The river is fast, undammed,
Rapunzel's hair let down
and won't allow this
shrub-steppe plain to climb it.
The river won't lend itself
to grow a tree. Look—
sagebrush flush with its banks.
No meeting, no kiss, no marriage.
Look at the tumbleweeds.
The river bathes in its glory,
the desert eats dust. The river
belongs to somewhere else.
The mighty river passes, not touching.
But not untouched.

COYOTE

*Pronunciation: \ kī-ō'-tē, chiefly Western kī'-ōt *

After years away,
I met you again on the tongue
of an old friend from home. *Kī'-ōt.*

Trotting through sagebrush. Wild
by any name. I'd moved to a green isle city
that pronounced you *kī-ō'-tē*

and abandoned you by the side of the road.
I'd forgotten your silver, slope-shouldered form
and gaze.

You're not a citizen of language or memory,
but I am. Changing your name
was a betrayal of home

born of living among outsiders,
born of looking back through outsiders' eyes
at interchangeable houses landscaped

with wishing wells and pansies.
I could never love the brown hills around us.
Now, in the city, who can love the desert in me?

Kī'-ōt. Kī-ō'-tē. You live outside pronunciation.
I'm become like you
and can't say your name either way.

Reprinted from Plume, *published by the University of Washington Press, 2012.*

HAROLD TAW's debut novel, *Adventures of the Karaoke King* (2011), is a karaoke grail quest about people who keep falling just short of their dreams. His writing has been featured on NPR, in a *New York Times* bestselling anthology and in *The Seattle Times*, and has garnered screenwriting awards. Harold is currently completing a novel set in Southeast Asia and is collaborating on a musical with the leaders of the Seattle chamber-pop band Poland.

THE REPOSITORY OF
BROKEN DREAMS

The boy should not have told his parents that his red double-decker bus had gone missing.

His father dumped the contents of the boy's rolling case onto his mother's bed until race cars and giraffes were jumbled together with books, crayons, and underwear. His mother called the front desk, and cleaning ladies arrived to peer under beds. He was marched back and forth until he knew every carpet fiber in the hallway between his mother's and father's rooms. Then his parents yelled at each other.

But the boy hadn't "lost" his bus. It had been driven away.

Riding to the end of the line anywhere was better than being locked in a luxury tower while his parents argued about which weekends he spent in two new places that weren't home. They bought him ice cream and gummy worms and sticker books. And left him alone with the television remote control.

After his mother fell asleep, the boy slipped out of bed and padded to the floor-to-ceiling windows. The hotel room was an aerie of iron and glass that looked down on headlights floating by like candles in a stream. Had his bus launched itself into the glittering darkness? Had it tired of jostling passengers, the road's grime, the sun and the fog?

Lost in gloomy thoughts, the boy at first heard only the wind spattering rain on the windows. But he soon noticed, faint and distinct, the sputtering of an engine and the clacking of a ticket machine.

The sounds emitted from the mini fridge.

The boy extracted soda pop, chocolate, and cheese wedges. He tapped the back wall of the fridge.

Nothing.

He used the heel of his hand to thump harder.

Nothing. And then...

A clatter of hooves against wood.

He looked to his mother, but her forearm was draped over her eyes. He turned back and encountered, inside the mini fridge, a goat head peering at him quizzically.

No, not a goat's head—a giant antelope's. Or more precisely, a nyala's. It had fan ears and spiral horns that curved upward like football goal posts. It pulled backward but its horns caught on a shelf. The animal whinnied in misery.

The boy reached out to pet the nyala on a furry, white chevron between its eyes.

"Ah!" he said. "You're so cute!"

The nyala snorted but was not displeased. More calmly this time, it attempted to extricate itself. Again its horns caught on a wire rack. The boy caressed the nyala's muzzle and scratched at the base of its horns. It emitted a contented sigh.

"If I help you out of the fridge," the boy said, "will you help me find my red double-decker bus?"

The animal's head tilted in contemplation. It grunted an assent.

The boy slid the shelving out and stooped to enter the mini fridge. He yanked down on the nyala's horns to ensure the points cleared the rear opening.

"Chin down!" he said. "Like you're doing a somersault. Now back up."

The animal was free. And the boy, clinging onto the nyala's horns, was pulled through the portal too. A flick of its powerful head and the boy landed on the beast's shaggy neck.

The nyala emerged from a burned-out tree stump into the midday sun. It set out through a meadow on a game path. Descending into a ravine, the nyala exited a wooded thicket and followed a road until they reached a covered bus stand. A baby doll, wearing long underwear stitched to her plastic skin, sat there quietly, her painted-on smile beginning to chip.

A red double-decker bus arrived with a squeak of brakes. That it was *his* red double-decker bus, grown life-sized, was unmistakable. The roof was torn off and the advertising placard had been scribbled out with purple crayon.

There was no driver and, apparently, no fee. The baby doll preceded them and was issued a ticket by a clacking machine, as were he and his nyala. The boy guided the beast up the stairs so it could turn its head freely in the open air. A pink teddy bear was already seated on the second level, trailing its paw over the railing.

Thickets alternated with tall grasses that rippled in the wind like a green-gold sea. The bus stopped periodically for new passengers—here, a stuffed lion, there, a robot with a missing arm. The bus hadn't, the boy realized, run away at all. It had found a place where it was needed.

Near sunset the bus arrived at a low, sandstone building that spread out in zigzags to pen in, with every right-angle turn, sprawling gardens. The toys disembarked and formed a ragtag line. Walking, rolling, limping, they moved single file on a path toward a bluff where seagulls wheeled in the sky.

The nyala carried the boy in the opposite direction to the inn's entrance.

The boy nearly mistook the child behind the front desk for an old man. Though the skin on his face was smooth, it was mottled and weathered by the sun. At the child's feet, a graying nyala snored atop a bed of straw.

"You may cut hay from the grounds." The child handed the boy a heavy key. "There's a scythe on the back stoop. Or let your nyala graze in the courtyard. Just make sure you're locked indoors by nightfall."

"Why?" the boy said.

"A nyala was taken from the central garden." The child grimaced. "Soulcatchers don't kill nyalas immediately. They prefer to devour them alive, piece by piece and joint by joint, from eyeballs to tongue to hooves."

"And children?"

The withered child shook his head. "They've no taste for human flesh. But a paired child feels the gnash of their teeth." He tapped his chest. "In here."

Other children greeted the boy in the inn's long corridors. Some boys remained mounted atop their massive beasts indoors. But the girls' nyalas—little more than striped deer with large ears—were too slight to bear such weight. The children were friendly enough but disappeared behind bolted doors, no one offering to help settle him in.

The boy filled his nyala's water trough and picked brambles from its coat. Then he fell into a deep, dreamless slumber. So fatigued was he by the day's journey, he didn't stir when his nyala bayed at the shaking windows, which dripped with viscous black fluid that evaporated in the first light of dawn. And his nyala, lacking words, could not describe it the following morning.

The freedom of his perfect days made up for the confinement of the long nights.

Every morning, the boy and his nyala boarded his bus and rode the entire route, disembarking wherever they pleased. The boy collected shells at the beach, strung garlands at waterfalls, listened to monkeys chatter in the jungle, waded into rivers shimmering with fish. From time to time, they saw in the distance nyala herds that fled at their approach.

The boy was happy but lonely. He tried inviting other children along. Most politely declined. The ones who accepted were too enraptured by playing with their own toys to take interest in him or their exotic destinations.

The boy also discovered that most children wandered off after a few days to be replaced by newcomers. Their abandoned toys shambled in later, either on foot or as passengers on his red double-decker bus, always disappearing down the well-worn path to the bluff. The boy couldn't help but develop a genial disinterest in the other children's comings and goings.

He might have proceeded this way forever were it not for the girl. She boarded his bus every third day. Her nyala was a jumpy creature that gnawed at a bare spot near its rump that had shredded into a festering sore. Not once did the girl greet him. At times, she gazed with unguarded hostility at everything and everyone. She always got off at the waterfall stop carrying a basketful of flowers.

The boy grew curious about what toy the girl concealed. Evenings of research in the inn's library yielded an answer.

The boy boarded his bus one morning with saddlebags of blossoms strapped to his nyala. He didn't immediately follow the girl. He waited until the vehicle had made its turnabout and returned to the waterfall bus stop. He and his nyala wended through dense foliage until they reached a glassy pool dappled in sun and shade.

The girl sat cross-legged on the sinuous roots of a banyan tree that cradled her like a nest. A unicorn's head rested in the girl's lap, the point of its silver horn a millimeter from her chin. Strewn about them were flower petals. The girl's nyala trembled, legs splayed, torn between huddling close to its mistress and fleeing.

The girl and the unicorn both had their eyes closed in blissful repose. Then two sets of eyes—human and equine—opened as one.

The boy was prepared for the unicorn's charge. As his nyala dipped its head to wield its spiral horns, he tore open a saddlebag and spilled its contents.

Neither he nor his nyala was impaled.

The unicorn had vanished. The girl snorted like a horse, eyes flashing at the cascade of flowers that streamed down from his nyala's belly like rainbow entrails. In her lap was a porcelain unicorn figurine that strained and bucked.

The boy kneeled and offered her flowers. The girl ate blossoms ravenously from his open palms.

The boy and the girl took to spending sunsets at the base of the bluff near the inn, a fallen tree above the tide line serving as a bench. From there, they watched toys hurtle off the cliff onto jagged rocks pounded by surf. Raggedy Ann dolls, plastic bulldozers, electronic pianos, stuffed tigers, ceramic tea sets—all pinwheeled down from the sky like geese riddled with buckshot. The detritus of a thousand abandoned toys littered the shore and floated in the sea.

"In front of everyone else, they act like their toys are the most precious things in the world," the girl said. "Then something shiny and new comes along. They don't care what happens to their toys, or their nyalas, after they leave."

"You remember nothing of the other place?" the boy said.

"I remember too much," she said. "At least our monsters come out only at night."

The girl waved flies away from her nyala's wound. Her nyala anxiously eyed the tiny porcelain unicorn that pawed the sand nearby. Even in its unmanifested form, the unicorn was fearsome—more feline than equine. A horned tiger.

"Whenever I feel weak," she said, "I sneak out and watch the soulcatchers at work. Come with me tonight. You'll remember. And stay."

"It's prohibited," he said. "They'll devour our nyalas."

"We'll lock our nyalas inside," she said. "Without our nyalas, we're shadows like them. We'll travel faster. Unnoticed."

The boy's nyala pressed against him, panting and whining. He stroked the beast's mane absently.

The boy's nyala battered the bathroom door with its horns and hind hooves. If it hadn't been for the door's metal bands—which must have been installed for this very purpose—the timbers would have shattered.

The girl took his hand and they slipped into the courtyard. Immediately he felt the change come over him. Without his nyala, his body vanished and he became indistinguishable from the night. The boy and the girl were conjoined shadows flitting as quickly over the veld as they did over the mountains.

They slackened their pace as a stench filled the air—blood, urine, feces, and fur. Inside a pen were nyalas packed so tightly they couldn't turn. Shadows fed the creatures one by one into a metallic chute of a massive machine with rotating cogs. From inside echoed the whir of blades, the crunch of bones, and the wail of nyalas.

The boy and the girl hid behind a boulder. They were at the other end of the meat grinder, at a cleaner place, where double doors swung open to expel items into a hamper. As they watched, a princess doll, replete with tiara, pink dress, and flowing blonde hair dropped onto a pile of brand new toys. Next came a radio-controlled car. Next a portable music player.

"Is this what happens to all abandoned nyalas?" he whispered to the girl.

"Only the gentlest thing," she said. "Some are not allowed to die. I'll show you."

"I've seen enough."

They made their way back to the inn more slowly, each lost in personal musings. The boy wondered whether pleasure must always be purchased by pain. Would he have chased his red double-decker bus into this world if it had already been marked and mangled by another child? If he ripped open his toys, would he find his parents' love inside? Could their love withstand exposure to the open air?

He knew what the girl would say. He asked her anyway.

She didn't answer. She wasn't there.

The boy had the sensation of being touched all over his body by insect legs. With nips and pinches, his incorporeal existence was being picked apart by feeding minnows.

"What do we matter to you without our nyalas?" The boy meant to shout, but his voice was wan and reedy.

Her nyala is half mad. It has no use and will be expelled. Unpaired, it cannot survive.

"No," the boy said. "I will care for her nyala as if it were my own. It will be safe, fed, warm."

Let the beast come for her. Then she can leave.

"She'll never leave."

Then she will become one of us.

The boy blanched. To be forever a ghost with a hole in its stomach, feeding upon the nyalas of others. Were he and the girl destined to become what they despised?

"Not while her nyala lives," he whispered.

The darkness coalesced, then burst into oily droplets. The boy felt chilled, soiled, raw. But the soulcatchers said no more. He was alone.

The boy reached the inn at daybreak. He retrieved his scythe and cut fresh grass. When he opened the bathroom door, his nyala stared as if he were an apparition. Then it knocked him over with rough licks to his face. It rolled in the spilled grass like a puppy, spiral horns clanking against the clay floors.

For three days the girl's nyala wouldn't eat or drink. The beast threw itself at the bathroom door until it was bruised and cut. On the fourth day, the boy tethered her nyala to his and set out for the swimming hole. There they found an emaciated unicorn lying barely conscious on its side. The girl's head was next to the unicorn's on the muddy bank, her body dangling into the water.

The boy dribbled fluid from crushed rose petals onto her lips. He slipped into the pool and embraced her until she awoke gasping.

The girl and her nyala accompanied him to the portal. When they stepped off the bus, the boy sadly patted the vehicle's sideboard. Perhaps nothing animated by blood could live forever.

They led their nyalas through the meadow in silence. The girl tied her beast to a nearby tree. The boy led his nyala to the burned-out stump before unsheathing his scythe.

"And if I set my nyala free?" the boy said.

"Once unpaired, it will be as 'free' as the other abandoned nyalas. It won't budge from this spot and will be taken. Soulcatchers aren't nourished by flesh. They subsist on suffering."

"Then what I do is a kindness?"

"Believe what you like."

The boy blinked away tears that his nyala licked away like honey droplets. He pressed his forehead to the beast's and eased it into a kneeling position. It gazed at him throughout with gentle eyes.

Grabbing the scythe's handles, the boy pulled the blade across his nyala's throat. Clean warm blood spattered him. The beast crumpled, surrendered. The boy buried his face in the nyala's bloody mane. The girl shut the animal's eyelids.

"Do you forgive me?" the boy asked her.

"Yes," she said.

"Will you join me?"

The girl looked at her nyala. The creature's nostrils flared and it bleated in distress. The girl shook her head. "You will see. The soulcatchers rule there as here."

The boy and the girl grasped hands for a moment. Then he stripped off his bloody clothes. The boy ducked naked through the portal.

WRITING TO ROCK

Imagined postcard adventures inspired by Pearl Jam

826 Seattle is lucky to have good friends. Among them is Pearl Jam bass-ist Jeff Ament, who not only has been a supporter of our efforts since the beginning, but also recently joined forces with Seattle-based guitar maker Mike Lull to donate to 826 Seattle the auctioned proceeds of two bass gui-tars he custom-painted.

Inspired by this generosity and Pearl Jam's recent twenty-year anni-versary, students from 826 Seattle's after-school tutoring program partici-pated in a week-long writing workshop during their mid-winter break to flex their writing muscles and learn more about the band. Students first researched information about one of the band's many international tour-ing destinations, then wrote postcard tales back to 826 Seattle that put the band on center stage in those places. The stories were written from the point of view of actual Pearl Jam band members, adoring fans, opening acts, or even microphones.

The workshop culminated with Jeff himself stopping by during after-school tutoring to hear the authors read their stories aloud and to hang out with the newest members of his fan club.

EDOM ARAYA is ten years old and goes to Adams Elementary. She likes listening to music and dancing to her favorite song, the Chipmunks' cover of "Single Ladies." One day, she will be a famous ballet dancer or a karate master.

A CHIPMUNK IN A CITY THAT HE DOESN'T KNOW

Dear 826 Seattle,

Greetings from Asmara, Eritrea! You'll never believe what happened! It all started at the Expo site at Asmara. The Expo site is one of my favorite places in Eritrea because there is a lot to do there. I go there a lot with my uncle and cousins to watch movies, eat fish and bread, drink coffee with milk, and watch knife dancers perform.

Anyway, I had gone to the Expo site this time to see Pearl Jam play. The opening act was the Chipmunks singing "Single Ladies." I was eating some kitcha fit-fit—a spicy bread—with a spoon and trying hard not to spill it on my new pink dress. All of a sudden, it started to rain very heavily, and a big wind came and blew the lead Chipmunk away! He was so little, and the wind was too strong for him. He blew right past a Gabaza set up at the Expo site. (Gabazas looks like igloos made out of straw, and they are traditional houses in the Eritrean countryside.)

Just then, 190 bicycle riders zoomed past the Expo grounds. They were racing in the Tour of Eritrea. The Chipmunk was blowing right toward them.

"*Kes belie!*" I yelled in Tigrinya ("Watch out!"). I didn't want the Chipmunk to get hit. I had been hit by a bicycle one time when I was seven, and I knew how bad it hurt.

They were about to crash, when all of a sudden, the Pearl Jam bass player, Jeff Ament, who just happened to be driving to the Expo Center to perform next, slammed on the brakes, jumped out of the car, and picked up the Chipmunk. He was just in time.

"What kind of animal is this?" he said, holding the Chipmunk in his arms.

The Chipmunk tried to answer, but he was still too scared. His heart was pounding, *boom, boom, boom*. Jeff wrapped the Chipmunk in a scarf, and put him in the car. Jeff was a part-time doctor as well as a musician, so he checked the Chipmunk to make sure he was okay. The Chipmunk's heart was still beating strongly, so Jeff called the emergency workers just to be safe. The emergency workers came and gave the Chipmunk a shot.

"He'll be okay," they said. "Just give him space." They took him to the hospital where he could rest.

Because the Chipmunk was going to be okay, Pearl Jam decided to go ahead and play the concert. There was a parked Boeing 727 plane in the Expo Center, so Jeff said, "Let's do the show on top of the plane!"

I clapped my hands. *That's an awesome idea to do the show on the plane*, I thought.

For the very last song, Pearl Jam started to play "Oceans," because we were near the Red Sea. At the last minute, the Chipmunk came back from the hospital, climbed up on the plane, and sang with the band! The people in the crowd were screaming because they were happy to see him again.

As I danced, I thought, *this is the best day ever*.

Wish you were here!

Love,
Emma

MELAT ERMYAS is eleven years old and goes to Eckstein Middle School. She is a bookworm herself and plans to one day write a story that will change people's perspective of the world. She finds inspiration for her writing from her favorite kinds of music: hip-hop, R & B, and Ethiopian music.

FIASCO IN NEW YORK

Dear 826 Seattle,

Greetings from the Big Apple! You'll never believe what happened! One sunny day in New York, I got a call from a New York operator who had a message for me.

"Pearl Jam is going to come to the Brooklyn Bridge to see the Bookworms play!" he said. I quickly hung up and sent an email to all of my friends, because I was the band leader for the Bookworms and all my friends were in the band. Even though I had sent an email to all my friends, I called them as quickly as I could and I told them what I had just been informed about.

Soon my friends and I were getting ready for the concert at the Brooklyn Bridge. We got the food and new rocking clothes. Then we called every single person we knew: family members, cousins, friends, and other relatives. Soon everyone knew that we were going to open for Pearl Jam at the Brooklyn Bridge. We practiced five hours a day, every day, until we were perfect. But even though we felt we were perfect, we practiced some more, because we were really nervous and we wanted to get even better!

It felt like only an hour of practice but soon the big day had arrived. We drove to the Brooklyn Bridge, pronto. But when we got there, people were in front of the bridge holding Pearl Jam signs instead of the Bookworms! We got out of the van and asked the person nearest to us, "Why is everyone holding Pearl Jam signs, when they should be holding *our* signs?"

The person turned around and said, "Pearl Jam is going to play at the Brooklyn Bridge, not you!"

It had turned out that what the operator had *really* said was that Pearl Jam was going to play at the Brooklyn Bridge, not the Bookworms! But it wasn't my fault because the operator was a New Yorker and New Yorkers talk *really* fast, so it's hard to tell what they are saying. In the end, though, Pearl Jam let us play for them and the crowd.

Wish you were here!

Your rock star,
Melat Ermyas

ROWAN MURRAY is thirteen and attends Whitman Middle School. In the future, he hopes to become a teacher or an actor—or maybe both. He enjoys many pursuits, such as songwriting, poetry, and singing. He finds inspiration from all facets, including music, the ocean, and the people and dogs in his life.

DECEPTION IS A DISH
BEST SERVED COLD

Dear 826 Seattle,

Greetings from the Las Vegas strip. You'll never believe what happened. I just had one of the best cases in years. It all started at a Pearl Jam concert. The band was playing, and everybody was having a good time. Lights glowed and giant light-up poker chips illuminated the stage.

Then it happened.

For the grand finale they were supposed to spray poker chips out into the crowd, but instead there was a powerful explosion. Chips sprayed the crowd, one of which hit a gentleman in the eye. His name was Brooks Gelato. He was taken away quickly via an ambulance to have his eye examined.

Pearl Jam hastened to the hospital to apologize to him. They said they hadn't meant for it to explode so hard. The doctors said his eye was going to be okay but the medical bills were going to be explosive. As Pearl Jam prepared to leave, Brooks called them over and said, "I'm going to sue the rock star pants off you, Eddie Vedder. I'll get you my pretty, and your little band too."

Eddie and I have been friends since the old days of high school. Then I went off to law school and he went to an arts college. He knew I was a very successful lawyer, so he promptly called me. As well as a lawyer, I was a pretty good private eye. A PI is a person you call if you don't want the flatfoots getting involved, and Eddie smelled something rotten. He thought foul play might've been involved. He didn't want Brooks getting angry though, so he called me.

I reviewed the case. It was all in Brooks' favor. But the pumps that shot out the poker chips appeared to have been tampered with, and this legal eagle didn't like the smell of it.

I talked to the man who had been in charge of loading the pumps. He seemed quite nervous under my shrewd and powerful gaze and he soon cracked like the egg he was. He said an unknown person had bribed him to add extra pressure. When I asked him about this anonymous villain, he said he didn't know. "He was wearing a wide-brimmed hat and a dark overcoat. It was night," he squealed.

I wondered, *Hmm, who would've done this?* Somebody who had a grudge against Pearl Jam. So, I pondered and pondered. Then, something about what he said came back to me. He said someone had bribed him with three million dollars. That meant the villain had to be a multi-millionaire. It also meant the villain had something to gain from having Gelato sue Pearl Jam.

I looked at the case and thought about who would gain from Pearl Jam being sued. There was A: Brooks Gelato—he'd get a lot of money. And B: His lawyer—he'd get a big fat payoff for winning the case. I thought we could count out Brooks right away. He got hit in the eye with a poker chip. He obviously didn't want that to happen.

That left the lawyer. I sent out one of my scouts, a certain John Bond. He reported back to me saying that the lawyer seemed as innocent as a newborn baby. That left Brooks. I thought and thought. Maybe he had a pain tolerance and he just wanted the big fat payoff? But still, it seemed a little dangerous. He could've lost an eye. I sent Bond to talk to the security people from the concert. Maybe they knew something. He came back with a tape.

"Sir, I have a video of what happened that night at the concert. It shows people being pelted," Bond said.

Brooks was in the front row. I reviewed the tape and found him. I slowly played it back. It showed the poker chips exploding out of the pump. They certainly hit many parts of Brooks' body, but they never hit his eye.

"Curious," I muttered. "Good job, Bond. You deserve a reward. I have a friend over in England who needs a spy. I'll call her. You should change your name though. Maybe, James?" I went back to the tape. The next bit really took the cake. I saw Brooks take a packet of ketchup and slap his eye, causing it to pop. The red liquid looked remarkably like blood. I put two and two together. It was pretty easy to see what had happened.

At the courthouse the next morning, I showed my tape to the jury and explained what had happened. I played the tape in slow motion. It showed Brooks pulling the ketchup from a concealed pocket from inside his jacket and crushing it against his eye.

"AHHHH," he yelled on the tape, clutching his face. I restrained myself from laughing. (It looked funny in slow motion—so sue me! On second thought, I don't advise it. *I'm* the legal eagle.)

Suddenly, Brooks panicked and ran out of the courthouse.

"After him!" I cried, and eight policemen followed me in the ensuing chase. Brooks' private car took him to the docks of Lake Powell where his yacht awaited. I leapt onto the ship and barely made it. The police were left on the dock.

"Give it up, Gelato, you're about to get licked," I said. "See what I did there? Gelato. Ice cream. Lick? Get it?" I laughed for a minute.

Gelato was not amused. "I haven't heard *that* one before," he said sarcastically.

I jumped and pinned Gelato to the ground. We wrestled for a moment. He slugged me; I slugged him. He stuck his finger up my nose. I flicked him in his supposedly injured eye. That's when he went for his slingshot and poker chips.

"These poker chips are filled with blinding poison!" he said. He shot a few chip at me. I dove into the expensive lavatory, and locked the door behind me.

"What can I do?" I muttered to myself.

I saw the toilet seat made out of gold. Then, it occurred to me. I broke off the toilet seat, smashed down the door and ran at Gelato with the toilet seat affixed to my arm like a shield. He shot at the golden target, but the chips bounced off harmlessly. I rammed into him, knocked him out, stole his slingshot, and dragged him along behind me. I went up to the control room and told the captain to turn the ship around. We went back to the dock.

Gelato was swiftly put behind bars and he admitted to the whole thing. He had bribed the pump man to increase the pressure of the pumps. He had also bribed his doctor to say he'd been hit in the eye.

Pearl Jam had more concerts that week. I went to several of them.

After the final concert, I went to the jail to see what had happened to Gelato. To my astonishment, the guards told me that just hours before, Gelato had knocked out a guard, and smashed through a window.

Apparently, as Gelato had jumped, he'd laughed maniacally, "See ya, imbeciles! Tell the Legal Eagle he can go sit in a tree and sue the pigeons for all I care!" Then he jumped.

Except, he was five-stories up. So let's just say he got the death penalty.

I got a heavy payoff from Pearl Jam, who thanked me gratefully for helping them and gave me an unlimited pass to all of their concerts. My family members are fans too, so they were happy as well.

This is Rowan Murray, signing off. And remember, if you ever need a lawyer, the Legal Eagle is here.

Sincerely,
Rowan Murray

LANGDON COOK is a writer, instructor, and lecturer on wild foods and the outdoors. His books include *Fat of the Land: Adventures of a 21st Century Forager* (Mountaineers, 2009), which the *Seattle Times* called "lyrical, practical and quixotic," and *The Mushroom Hunters: On the Trail of an Underground Economy* (Ballantine, in press, 2013). His writing has appeared in *Sunset, Gray's Sporting Journal, Outside, The Stranger,* and *Seattle Magazine,* among others. Langdon lives in Seattle with his wife and two children.

CRAB FEED

When friends from out of town come to visit, I like to give them the opportunity to feel awkward, get dirty, and maybe even impale themselves on a sharp object. I feed them crab. A fresh-caught mess of Dungeness crabs in the shell offers all these advantages, not to mention the reward of sweet, sought-after meat that is as much a feature of the West Coast as the blue crab is of the East—only better.

The setup is simple: newspaper on table, boiled crab on newspaper, beer in hand. There was a time when I melted sticks of butter and left a can of Old Bay out, but I'm over such garish additives now. Crab wants to be eaten *neat.*

Perhaps it's only fair to acknowledge the butter debate. I'll admit that I enjoy dunking lobster in hot melted butter as much as the next person, and I suppose it's not heresy to do the same with Dungeness. Certainly blue crab needs an extra boost, all the better with garlic and cream, but I usually refrain with our native Pacific crab. A fisherman I know insists on the cheater. "My dad taught me how to eat crab," Steve declared once, red in the face, when we were covering this ground yet again. "He'd have the ramekin of butter, and the big pieces he'd dip. The small pieces got tossed into the ramekin. Then at the end...." Steve paused to imagine the last bits of crab being stirred around in slightly congealed butter until they were all caught up on the tines of his fork. He sighed.

I'm not trying to ruin any childhood memories. Even I will eat Dungeness crab with butter on occasion. The point is, you don't have to. The meat is so succulent and pleasing to the palate in its suppleness that it can be eaten right out of the shell without even the slightest regret for a lack of condiment. Sucking the claws and legs of their juices is the very essence of eating Dungeness crab. When you eat crab with the right people, the room is filled with yips and low moans and slurping sounds and countless other audible expressions of ecstasy.

Invariably there's one guest who will insist on wearing a crab bib—just as his father or grandfather had years earlier—but I gave up long ago trying to prevent crab juice and fragments of shell from spraying me head to toe, never mind the newsprint that rubs off on hands and arms like smudgy prison tattoos. It's a dirty business, eating crab, and not for the squeamish. My only nod to my more fastidious guests is a roll of paper towels on the table.

You need a big pot for a mess of crabs—a bubbling cauldron, really. Such cookery brings out the witches and warlocks in us all, and I'll admit to taking some ghoulish pleasure in dragging credulous crab-eaters into the kitchen for the moment of truth: the tossing of live crabs into the boil. Though that high-pitched whine isn't really the screaming of the crabs but rather the sound of air whistling out of their shells, the effect is always the same. I feel bad about this moment, too. Really.

The cooked crabs are brought out on platters and dumped in the middle of the papered table. Armfuls of cold beer in the bottle are hustled out as well. Eating crab and drinking beer go hand in hand, and the more beer the less self-conscious the guests will be about cracking shells, ripping off claws, splattering each other, and combing through tall shell middens for elusive nuggets.

Breaking the cooked crabs down into edible chunks isn't as difficult as one might think. The carapace, fiery orange after boiling, is the first to go. It comes off easy with a little leveraging on the hindquarters. The guts will usually slide away with the shell, and what's left of them can be scraped off along with the lungs. After you snap the body in half, the two mirror sections are ready for eating. Each leg can now be separated as a segmented piece, with a good chunk of meat exposed at the joint where the leg was formerly attached to the body. Claws often require a cracker—or a swift blow from an empty beer bottle.

All this work is paid back handsomely. For the neophyte, the first bite is usually a revelation. How can a scuttling insect of the sea be so tender and delicious? Even seasoned crab eaters are stirred in primal, unexpected ways, making a crab feed a loose and unpredictable event.

Reputedly named after a small, defunct fishing village on the Strait of Juan de Fuca in Washington State, Dungeness crabs inhabit coastal waters from Alaska's Aleutian Islands to Monterey Bay, California. They can grow to ten inches across the carapace, though an eight-inch span is more common.

The crabs begin life by hatching out of eggs carried on the abdomen of the female in a mass known as a sponge, with a large female caring for up to two and a half million eggs. After hatching, the young are free-swimming, or planktonic. Over the next year they go through several larval, shrimplike stages before molting into their familiar crab form as juveniles.

Crabs are reproductively mature at two to three years. As adults they scavenge the bottom, feeding on clams, mussels, shrimp, small fish, and dead animals. They move into shallow water to mate in the spring, with the male clasping the female face to face in a sort of wrestler's clinch, waiting for her to molt so he can penetrate the soft abdomen and deposit his sperm. The female will then carry the sperm with her for up to several months, not fertilizing the eggs until she extrudes them from her abdomen, at which point she buries herself in the sand until the eggs hatch. Aside from humans, the crab's main predators include bottomfish such as halibut, dogfish, and sculpins, as well as octopuses, sea otters, and other crabs. Salmon and other finned fish feed on them as larvae.

Commercial harvest began in the mid-1800s in the San Francisco Bay. Today the haul is nearly forty million pounds. The crabs are most commonly caught in steel traps called pots, which are baited with smelly gobs of fish heads, sardines, or even cat food. But there are other ways to skin a crab.

A while back, when my friend Ivar (no connection to Seattle's legendary "acres of clams" chowder magnate) flew in from Boston for a wedding, he asked if he might join me on a crabbing expedition. Ivar really wanted to eat some fresh crab while in town, and he knew I had some opinions on the subject.

My approach to this time-honored Puget Sound ritual is a little different from most. For one thing, I don't use a crab pot. We pulled into the dive shop in Mukilteo so Ivar could rent a wetsuit.

"You're joking, right?"

Not in the least. I suppose it might be easier to paddle a little inflatable raft a hundred yards offshore and drop a pot, but the chase for me is half the fun, maybe more than half. Catching my own food in the wild, if only occasionally, feels like a reasonable response to the mind-numbing chore of pushing a shopping cart down the fluorescent-lit runways of a supermarket.

I tried to explain this to Ivar. We sat in the car and I told him about my first dive in pursuit of crab. It was a wild, exhausting swim in the Sound (I didn't mention the "exhausting" part) as I stalked the crabs through waving pastures of eelgrass near Golden Gardens beach in Seattle. The crabs scuttled, paddled, and otherwise skedaddled with remarkable alacrity when pursued, using their legs like flippers to effect their characteristic sideways scrambles to safety. I cruised the surface looking for them, sometimes diving and swimming along the bottom, where there was less resistance and the freedom of the dive was held back only by the need for air. Crabs on the run disappeared into cloudy blooms of sand.

The best way to catch them, I painfully discovered through trial and error, was to chase them down like a seal, pin them against the bottom, and then carefully, out of reach of the flexing pincers, grab their hind legs. Even if the crabber is wearing a heavy neoprene glove, bigger males can inflict grievous retribution on a wayward pinky, sometimes even slicing through the glove completely to draw blood.

Sitting in the front seat, I carefully explained my methods to Ivar. I had learned a lot on these initial crab dives, and now I wanted to share my knowledge with an eager pupil. Our friend Karl was with us, too, in the backseat. Karl works with sea mammals at the Monterey Bay Aquarium, swimming with injured seals and helping to rehabilitate them back into the wild. Karl's last name is Mayer; he's been known as "Air" Mayer for as long as I've known him, for his habit of jumping off tall things. I once followed Karl seventy vertical feet over a waterfall into a chilly canyon pool, in perhaps one of the stupidest stunts of my life. In the salt he can dive deeper and stay under longer than just about anyone I know.

Ivar turned in his seat, pointing an accusatory finger at Karl. "You were in on this all along."

In the shop we looked through the suits without luck. Ivar is a large man. He played tackle on our college football team back east. I remember seeing a photograph of him taken for the school newspaper. In the picture Ivar is going over the top of a dogpile and looking straight at the camera lens. His arms are spread, hands ready to throttle the quarterback. His face looks like something out of a Halloween drive-in movie. It's a jarring picture: a man transformed into a wild, uncontrollable beast. Ivar's biceps are about the size of my thighs.

Mumbling, the shop clerk disappeared into the back, then reemerged with an extra-extra-large. After what seemed like a long time my friend came out of the dressing room, grousing about the tight fit. "It doesn't feel right," he said, more like a little boy.

"Yeah, but you look good." Karl slapped him on the back. It was true. All that bulk stuffed inside a tight blue neoprene casing made his muscles stand out even more than usual. Ivar looked like a superhero.

"What you need is a cape."

"It's really hot in here," Ivar complained.

Karl started to laugh. "No wonder, you big dummy. It's inside out."

Somehow Ivar had managed to put the suit on inside out and zip himself up by pulling the leash attached to the zipper. Now he was squeezed in so tight he couldn't get it undone. A look of panic crossed his face. Little beads of sweat were already forming on his forehead. He flailed his arms, trying to reach the zipper.

The three of us stood there in the shop, unsure of what to do next. Finally, Ivar broke the silence. "I'm freaking out. Get me a knife!"

Before Ivar could summon his gridiron strength to burst free, Incredible Hulk-style, we managed to wrestle the zipper down his neck and peel off the suit. He popped out with an audible sigh and wiped the sweat off his brow. "Whose idea was this?" he asked diffidently. "Can't we just buy some crab at the market like normal people?"

Then the clerk came back with the shop's lone triple-X, and we were off. The day was warming up, and we were ready to fall into the Sound's cool arms. Certainly Ivar was. His face was still red, and the sweat from his ordeal showed through his shirt.

We drove past the ferry dock and found a dirt access road that paralleled the railroad tracks. At the end of the road was a gravel parking lot. The tide was still out, and a few Vietnamese families were on the mudflats with buckets and rakes, digging clams. I had dug clams here, too, but recent shellfish advisories now discouraged against it. Soon this beach, like so many others within the clutches of the greater Seattle-Tacoma metro area, would be permanently closed to such activity. Our quarry today, however, moved in from deeper, cleaner waters to breed.

Even in a triple-extra-large wetsuit, Ivar felt squeezed and out of sorts. He walked down to the water with his arms sticking out at an odd angle. Putting on his fins took immense effort, as it involved bending and stretching the taut, elastic suit. I showed him how to spit in his mask and wash it out, but the mask quickly fogged anyway. He floated on his back in the water with his mask off, letting the refreshing sensation of the Sound pour into every nook and cranny.

"I think I'll just stay like this for a while."

"Put your face in the water," Karl commanded. "Use your snorkel." But Ivar didn't want to move. Finally he rolled over and did a dead man's float for a moment before popping up like a wounded seal. "It's claustrophobic in here. I feel like I'm made out of rubber."

Karl shook his head and swam out past the ferry dock while I tried to lead Ivar along the jetty, where it was shallow. Somehow water kept gushing into his mask, and he had to stop and readjust it. He drank a mouthful of the Sound. "Blow out like this," I said, spraying water from my snorkel. Ivar put his face in the water and blew.

"Maybe this wasn't such a good idea. I could always watch from the beach."

"Forget it. We need three limits of crabs. You're in."

After pointing out a few crabs, I encouraged Ivar to catch one. Diving for crabs in the mating season is like shooting tuna in a can, I told him. The males are preoccupied with finding females; they're out on the prowl and vulnerable. Ivar went under tentatively and came up with a snort, spitting water and bobbling a male Dungeness in his hands like a hot potato. The crab was trying to grab his fingers, and Ivar didn't know what to do. Keeping it bouncing in the air must have seemed like a good idea at the time. Both crab and captor waved their appendages madly, and if crabs can talk I'm sure this one was swearing like a sailor, just like Ivar.

I swam over and put the crab in my mesh bag. Ivar let out a shout, something between a whoop and a war cry, as if he had just clotheslined a running back at midfield. Farther out, we could see Karl diving like a porpoise and coming up minutes later with enormous crabs in each hand.

That night our friend John-O was having his wedding rehearsal and dinner at a swank downtown restaurant. Smartly, he'd neglected to invite any of us. Instead, we threw our own party at my place on Capitol Hill. Word must have leaked out, because the house was packed. Though my friends didn't know it yet, this was something of a last hurrah for me too. After renting a string of apartments and shared houses over the years, I would give up my bachelor ways at the end of the month to move in with Martha.

Ivar ran into the kitchen and called for more crabs. Our limit of eighteen seemed suddenly thin. Luckily I had a bunch more in the freezer from previous dives. To make the spoils go further, I started frying up crab cakes in the galley. Marty volunteered her sous chef services, as did our friend Emily, and we soon had the assembly line humming: Marty working a red-hot frying pan to sauté up veggies and Emily flipping the cakes, while I extracted crabmeat and threw together patties with whatever seasonings and condiments I could find. Even when the keg was kicked and Emily had finally relinquished her apron for a cool-down smoke outside, Marty and I were still taking orders, throwing big pads of butter in the sizzling pan and gobbing in patties of my signature cakes.

At last, when each and every finger-nicking shell had been exhumed and the final batch was plated, I came out of the hot kitchen. It was late.

Music blared and the living room overflowed with bodies in motion. Ivar and Karl were in a corner, regaling the same girl with increasingly heroic and danger-filled tales of their afternoon dive. The smell of cooked crab hovered in the air like a heavy, sweet fog. Though the beer was gone, there were new faces, fancy outfits, and expensive champagne all around. The wedding party had heard the news: a crab feed was on.

DUNGENESS CRAB CAKES

Cooking crab cakes should become quick and second nature after a couple of tries, and they're always a crowd-pleaser. The key to good crab cakes is a lot of crab. This may sound obvious, but if you've ever ordered them in a restaurant, even some fancy high-end joint, you know that chefs try to stretch their expensive crabmeat as far as possible by adding copious, often distracting fillers—one more reason to make your own.

That said, I like to experiment with different cake recipes to play with the flavor accents and consistency. Such experimenting, it should be noted, is far more economical when not paying fish-market prices. A solid presentation goes something like this.

1/2 cup diced onion
1/4 cup diced red pepper
2 tablespoons butter, divided
Freshly ground black pepper to taste
1 pound Dungeness crabmeat
2 heaping tablespoons chopped fresh parsley
1 large egg, beaten
1/2 cup quality bread crumbs, or more to taste
1 tablespoon fresh lemon juice
2 teaspoons Old Bay seasoning (optional)
1–2 tablespoons mayonnaise or Dijon mustard (optional)
1 tablespoon Worcestershire sauce (optional)
Lemon wedges for garnish

Sauté onion and red pepper in 2 tablespoons of butter. Add salt and black pepper to taste. In a mixing bowl, combine sautéed vegetables with crabmeat, parsley, egg, bread crumbs, lemon juice, and Old Bay seasoning. Add bread crumbs to taste, not all at once. If desired, add mayo or mustard and Worcestershire sauce. Go wild with the seasonings if you choose—with all the rubs and spice blends on the market these days, the sky's the limit. I stick with Old Bay. Also, additional bread crumbs can be used for dredging if preferred.

Next, form the patties. For firm patties, refrigerate for an hour or so on waxed paper, a step I usually omit due to the flying-by-the-seat-of-my-pants nature of my average crab feed. Then pan-fry in the remaining butter. Make sure you get a nice golden brown crust on the outside to contrast with the succulent inside. Serves 4

Copyright by Langdon Cook, from Fat of the Land: Adventures of a 21st Century Forager *(Skipstone, 2009)*

Photo by Langdon Cook

NAZRAWIT DESSIE is eleven and goes to Hamilton International Middle School. Her story was inspired by the 826 Seattle Adventure Postcard workshop. Nazrawit describes her biggest adventure as many people do: coming to 826 Seattle to work on writing! Soon, she plans to write another successful story.

CORN-A-GOOD SURPRISE

It all started one extremely hot day in Corn-a-Good. Corn-a-Good is a very good village in Ethiopia that has 333 people and very grassy places for animals to hide. Most importantly, corn was the most popular food in the village. My twin brother Alex and I had decided to go on vacation to Corn-a-Good to celebrate our graduation from college.

"Alex, Anna, you guys should go to Corn-a-Good because it's beautiful and I really want you to get to know that place," my mother had said when we were trying to decide where to go. She and my dad had grown up there. It was a long trip from our home in Seattle, but it was worth it.

One morning, a week after we arrived in Corn-a-Good, Alex, my uncle, and I were outside in the backyard at my uncle's farm. It was very hot. I was holding an ear of golden colored corn that Alex and I had won the night before at the raffle. The raffle was part of a special celebration because the president of Ethiopia had come for a visit and decided to have a game night for everyone to play and win prizes. We had won an ear of golden corn. It was worth 850 Birr (about $50).

"Why it is so expensive?" I asked my uncle.

"Probably because it tastes like ice cream with some chocolate and cherries on top!" my uncle said. People always ate the golden corn in Corn-a-Good when it was a special occasion.

Suddenly, our neighbors called our names to congratulate us on our win.

"Alex and Anna!" they said. "Congratulations!"

We put down our ear of golden corn and ran to where the neighbors were. When we came back, the golden corn was gone! We looked around and saw a Bleeding Heart baboon with brown fur that looked like the bark of an old tree stump. All of a sudden he ran away with our golden ear of corn, making funny monkey noises.

We called, "Stop, that's our corn!"

We jumped on our zebra, Mr. Z, and chased after the baboon. (We had gotten our zebra from our neighbors who didn't want him anymore because he took up too much space. However, we liked that he was big). We jumped onto Mr. Z because we thought he would be fast and that he could catch up with the baboon.

The Bleeding Heart baboon was climbing when a rock fell and hit the golden corn, but it didn't break. The corn fell and the baboon kept climbing. We picked up the golden corn and happily went home.

When we got home, we decided to have the golden corn for dinner. We were washing it when the golden corn split open and I saw a shiny and even *more* golden ear of corn inside. It looked like a star had popped out. It was real solid gold! Now we understood why it was worth so much money! We were so excited and happy.

We were still starving after our big adventure though, so Alex decided to call the neighbors for dinner. Surprisingly, he called the baboon to come as well. We put some real corn in a pot to cook and ate it all together. It was delicious.

LUCIA MINAHAN is thirteen years old and is a veteran of the 826 Seattle workshop scene. She has logged many weekend hours writing on varied topics such as alien journals, zoo-trip tales, and music criticism. She wrote this piece as part of the Adventures in Eating workshop.

MAKING FLAN

It is the morning after a cold summer's night (yes, summer). I wake up to a tangle of blankets, a musty smell only partially masked by detergent. Everybody else is out, my *abuelo*, my grandpa, on his morning walk, Mom, Dad, and Esther out in the hills.

Abuela, grandmama, is waiting for me with a plate of warm toast and homemade plum jam. She is dressed in a blue and white striped apron, her chestnut-dyed hair brushed back. I could attempt to find my friends from last year, but I stay with her instead. After all, I only get to see her once a year.

"I know what we'll do today." She smiles at me. "We'll make flan." I knew she was going to say this. She's been saying it for the past week, promising me that we'll make it today.

First, she pulls the sugar out of the wooden cabinet in the kitchen. I cover my finger with it to look like a marshmallow and suck on it until the crystal sweetness disappears. We cook the sugar with some water until it is a golden brown. This is one of my favorite parts; it looks so perfect in the pan, I could look at it forever. We coat the cylinder-shaped flan container with the caramelized sugar. It smells delicious.

"Now, why don't you go get the eggs for me." She smiles at me.

"Okay!" I say. I run over to the damp pantry and open the refrigerator door. I pull out a carton of eggs and carefully make my way back to the kitchen. Abuela cracks open the eggs for me. I'm too scared I'll ruin the flan with an eggshell. But she lets me beat them, spraying a little here and there. After that, I wash my hands.

"Mommy says that I can get sick if I get raw egg in my mouth," I say.

"Don't worry, nobody I know has gotten sick. Good job on the eggs!" she answers, patting me on the head.

Next, we pour the milk into the eggs. It is *La Asturiana*, the Spanish brand we go to buy in Burgos when we go grocery shopping every week or so. I slosh it around with a wooden spoon and watch how the daffodil yellow of the eggs and white of the milk swirl together.

We pour the mixture into the metal container where the sugar has hardened and I clamp down the hooks. Then, we put the almost-there flan into a pot filled with water where it will sit on the warm stove for an hour or so. We call this in Spanish the *baño Maria*.

An hour later, I come running from the living room. "Abuela, Abuela! Is it done yet?" I call.

"Okay, okay," she says softly. "I'll check."

She pulls out a small, silver knife from a drawer and lifts the top of the hot pot. A warm cloud of steam comes out of it. I stand on my tiptoes to see how she tests the flan. Carefully, she unlatches the top of the flan container and sticks the tip of the knife in.

"Well?" I say when she pulls it out.

"I think we've got ourselves a flan!" she says.

"*Yupi!*" I yell.

"Do you want to see it closer?"

"Yes!"

Abuela pulls the container out of the water with her worn, red pot-holders. I peer in and I can see the creamy yellow mixture, now hardened in the pot. I can smell the rich caramel flavor and the eggs.

"Now," she says, "we must let this sit out for a little while and then let it sit in the fridge until it is nice and cold."

The flan is delicious. When we pop it out of the container, all of the sugary sauce comes out and it smells like heaven. I feel so good after making it. Abuela and I have done a great job.

SHANNON BORG is a published poet with an MFA in poetry from the University of Washington and a PhD in poetry and literature from the University of Houston. She regularly writes about travel, food, and wine in the Pacific Northwest.

Photos by Harley Soltes

LORA LEE MISTERLY and her husband Rick bought land near Rice, Washington in 1981 and began selling their cheese in 1987. They now produce roughly 5,000 pounds of farmstead goat cheese per year. In 2002 they founded the Quillisascut Farm School of the Domestic Arts, with a focus on teaching culinary students and professionals about the farm-to-table connection. Today, more than eighty students and professional chefs visit their farm each summer.

WINTER DREAMING

From Thanksgiving through late April, almost six months, Quillisascut Farm is dormant on the surface; but below ground it's working, conserving energy, and getting ready for the next season. Winter is a beginning. In the middle of a cold, dry eastern Washington winter, especially on a small farm like this one, time seems to slow down. It's as if everything—the plants, the goats, the chickens, even the soil—is waiting to see what comes next. And the human members of this scene are waiting, too, for the slow season to pass.

"When the first killing frost comes in fall, you feel like you've lost your friends," says farmer and goat-cheese maker Lora Lea Misterly over a cup of tea in the bunkhouse kitchen on a snowy January afternoon. "The abundance is gone—the beans, the tomatoes. We've butchered the lambs. But then you start planning, thinking, and dreaming about next summer. Winter is an incredibly important time for us." By "us," Lora Lea means herself and her husband, fellow farmer Rick, but she's also thinking of the other residents of the farm—about forty Alpine Cross goats that do the majority of the "work" around this place, as well as a smattering of chickens, ducks, cats, and the farm's dogs—Libby, the white-dreadlocked komondor, and Jet, an eager border collie. She also would include every vegetable, tuber, fruit tree, grapevine, and worm on this land. "Everything is connected here," Lora Lea says. "The soil feeds the plants that feed us. We are merely the walking, talking result of that connection."

This is a different season in which to feel that connection. Most people visit Quillisascut and other farms in summer, when the fields are ripe, the animals graze, and the farm yards buzz with activity. The Quillisascut

Farm School of the Domestic Arts is in session then, too, when the garden is full to bursting with enough vegetables, fruits, and herby things to keep dozens of inventive chefs occupied and fed for weeks. Chef Kären Jurgensen is in the kitchen at the farm school every day; she keeps the students busy creating menus and meals, preserving fruit, and breaking down newly butchered animals. Lora Lea invites a steady stream of local farmers, ranchers, and other providers to visit and, in turn, takes the students to visit neighboring farms to help them understand the diversity and interconnectedness of her community. And, of course, Quillisascut is just like farms and farming communities across the country, living through seasonal cycles and making ends meet while producing the food we all eat.

To see the farm in winter is a stark contrast to its summer abundance. Outside, there are two feet of snow; everything is covered and huge, fluffy flakes are adding to the blanket. Inside, the large, bright kitchen is warm. A unique woodstove-and-pipe system sends hot water through pipes Rick embedded in the concrete floors, keeping the place toasty. Even so, the house seems to be holding its breath, waiting. But Lora Lea knows that although winter on the farm seems quiet, a lot is going on; it's just more subtle than the crazy excesses of summer.

The farm is silent in the insulating snow. Somehow this silence simplifies everything here. The large straw-bale bunkhouse with its salmon-colored stucco and red metal roof—built by Rick, Lora Lea, and friends as a place for the chefs and students to stay when they visit—is a bright contrast to the snow. Behind it on a large patio, the white-stucco-and-brick wood-burning oven looks like an altar. It truly is one—a transformative place where countless pizzas and loaves of bread have been baked. (Miraculous rumors of as many as 120 loaves baked here in a single day circulate even in the restaurant kitchens of Seattle, three hundred miles away.)

Up a small hill stands the weathered brown barn where the goats, chickens, and other animals are hunkered down to ride out this most recent January storm. Nearby, the cheesemaking shed—two rooms devoted to milk storage, and making and aging cheese, big enough for a dozen students to work in—now stands empty. Gardens surround these

outbuildings, as well as a small vineyard and orchard, neither of which has been pruned yet, and the gnarled vines look like old trolls, their long canes draping to the ground like hair. Rick and Lora Lea's house, and another small house closer to the road, where Daisy Mae Boughey, Lora Lea's mother, lives, seem almost hidden. In all, most of the square footage of the buildings is devoted to the work of the farm. The farm itself is where the living goes on, year-round.

In the field below, a flock of two dozen Western Merriam wild turkeys bob toward the wooded hills—forward and back, almost single file, like a conga line in their black-and-white-feathered best. The chickens and goats are huddled inside the barn, but they chuckle and stir as they hear Lora Lea approach and open the gate. They're hoping for some tidbit, but also they seem curious, as though they don't want to miss anything.

The garden is a study in white and grey. Snow covers the mounded rows where a few months ago chard and kale, tomatoes and beans prospered in bright abundance. Now ocher-colored corn stalks speckled with black mold are bent over in their rows like piles of bones. Spiky sunflower stalks echo the grey-brown of the wooden fences. From the roof of the cheese shed, four-foot icicles reach halfway to the ground; it has been freezing cold on and off for weeks.

You can see things in winter that would go unnoticed during other times of the year. Here and there in the snow, small piles of jet-black, perfectly egg-shaped rabbit scat mark the paths of those quiet creatures, now snug in their burrows, sleeping the day away. Delicate deer tracks cross the property. Several old rusted farm implements stand out against the white like sculptures from another age. Round, black walnut pods stain the snow beneath their mother tree. A single, fluffy grey turkey feather stands out against a drift, its flat tip darker than the downy pinfeathers closer to the quill end.

Beyond the farm, the foothills of the Huckleberry Mountain range are soft, rolling, scattered with ponderosa pine, tamarack, Western larch, red fir, and the red branches of willow. The scene here is repeated on other farms in the area, all in the same state of stasis. Dick and Joan Roberson's fields of organic garlic are covered in snow, as are Jeff and Jeanette Herman's Cliffside Orchards and Stephan Schott's beehives. The unionized employees of Schott's Mingo Mountain Apiary are tucked away in their waxy cells, waiting until the sun warms their wings and grows their food. The trees in John and Janet Crandall's Riverview Orchard a few miles away are bare, but the orchard's other business, Crandall Coffee Roasters, is busy in winter, roasting beans and delivering them to cafes in nearby towns. A rich, smoky aroma floats over their frozen fields near their farm, a pungent reminder that the industrious farmers in this area must find creative ways to supplement their seasonal farming income.

THE WORK OF THE SOIL, THE WORK OF THE HOUSE

Below ground, even during this freeze, the soil is at work. Dig into it and in the rich tilth deeper down you can feel life and even warmth. The word *tilth* itself comes from the Middle English *tilian* ("to till" or "to labor"), and this soil is definitely laboring—its microbes working away, completing the seasonal cycle of their development. The rich browns and blacks of the compost pile are a stark contrast to all the white, and here is where the most activity is going on. Turn over a shovelful of earth: the steam rises—the soil is busier than the bees at this time of year, continuing to build itself.

Down the hill, inside the bunkhouse, it is a time of restoration, of dreaming and planning. As we enter the warm kitchen, the cold, clear, slightly smoky scent of the outside air is replaced with a range of smells—the meaty smokiness radiating all the way from the back room, where sausages and other cured meats are hanging on strings from a metal rack. Lora Lea is there and says, "Oh, you have to come and see the prosciutto." On the way through the bunkhouse, the smell of wood smoke from the stove mingles with the dusty, sunny aromas of the last of the season's tomatoes—picked from the vines green before the first freeze, now in various shades of pink and red, piled in baskets to slowly ripen. Lora Lea picks one up. "This is an Oxheart, see?" Yes, it has a pointed end, and it does resemble a heart—not a stylized valentine heart, but a real, bloody human heart.

That is how things are here, even in the quietest season—nothing is created just for show. This is a working farm, and the beauty around us is the authentic product of the work that is done. The back room is full of the season's final, quirky beauty—huge, knobby green squash, dozens of cobs of bright red corn peppered with deep purple kernels, hanging on their brittle stalks to dry. The riot of color is a contrast to the gentle greyness of the outside landscape. Here it is all about preserving the last of the harvest, extending its energies as long as possible.

Copyright by Shannon Borg and Lora Lea Misterly, from Chefs on the Farm: Recipes and Inspiration from the Quillisascut Farm School of the Domestic Arts *(Skipstone, 2008)*

JACOB'S CATTLE BEAN, KALE, AND CHÈVRE SOUP
Recipe by Chef Kären Jurgensen

Makes 8 servings

The goat cheese adds a delicious tang to this comforting soup. The heavy cream binds the beans together and makes the soup thicker, so resist the urge to substitute whole milk or half-and-half. Because of the heavy fat content, this soup freezes well.

Note: Canned beans are not a suitable substitute as the beans make their own stock.

2 cups (about 12 ounces) Jacob's Cattle beans or other white beans, rinsed and soaked overnight (3 parts water to 1 part beans, soaking water reserved)
2 tablespoons salt
2 tablespoons (1/4 stick) unsalted butter
1 medium carrot, diced
1 celery stalk, diced
1 medium yellow onion, diced
2 cloves garlic, finely chopped
1-1/2cups tomato purée
1 cup chopped preserved or purchased roasted red peppers
1 bunch black kale (or other kale), about 8 to 10 leaves, stemmed and chopped
2 dried bay leaves
1 tablespoon dried thyme
1 teaspoon red chili flakes
1 cup heavy cream
1-1/2 cups (about 3/4 pound) soft goat cheese
1 teaspoon freshly ground black pepper
Kosher salt

Put the beans and soaking water in a large stockpot over medium-high heat. Bring to a boil and skim foam from the beans. Reduce the heat to a gentle simmer and add the salt (the water should taste lightly of salt). Cook about 1 hour, until the beans are soft in texture and creamy in flavor.

In another saucepan, melt the butter over medium heat, add the carrot, celery, yellow onion, and garlic, and cook until the mixture is soft but not brown. Stir in the tomato purée, red peppers, and black kale. Cook for 4 to 5 minutes and add salt to taste.

When the beans have finished cooking, stir in the vegetable mixture, bay leaves, thyme, and chili flakes. Cook for about 20 minutes, then add the heavy cream, goat cheese, and black pepper. Cook for 15 minutes more, then season to taste with salt.

Variations: In summer use fresh tomatoes, peppers, and thyme. For a lighter minestrone-style soup, leave out the heavy cream and goat cheese.

Copyright by Kären Jurgensen, from Chefs on the Farm: Recipes and Inspiration from the Quillisascut Farm School of the Domestic Arts *(Skipstone, 2008)*

Photo by Harley Soltes

KIM VO is from Vietnam. She is seventeen and goes to Health Sciences and Human Services High School in Highline. She wrote this piece in Ms. Esrick's ELL class. Her fondest memory is of working on her essay with 826 volunteers and revising her work. Her goal is to go to college and find an exciting job.

THE POWER OF LANGUAGE

This is depressing, I have no idea what people are saying, I thought when I put my first step on this land, the United States. My family and I emigrated from Vietnam and came to Seattle last year. We faced a lot of difficulties after we arrived, like finding jobs and going to school. Language was the main obstacle that I had to face. Although I had studied English in my country before, I was shocked when I realized I could not understand what Americans were saying to me. I realized that being bilingual was important so I could communicate, feel safe and free, and learn about American culture. Then I could feel a part of my new country.

If you can communicate with words, you are powerful. Without words, you are locked inside yourself. The first time I went to school I just froze when people communicated—they talked too fast. It was scary because I couldn't tell them how I felt. When my teacher was teaching, I felt like an outcast. I didn't want to be laughed at just because I couldn't speak English. Studiously, I tried to learn English better and tried to create more relationships in school. I made friends and they helped me learn English. There were wonderful people in my school. Specifically, people here are more polite when they greet and leave by using some common idioms. They usually say, "How are you?" or "Have a good day!" or "Have a good weekend!" We don't say these things in Vietnam. We just say "*xin chao,*" (hello) and "bye bye." Being bilingual makes me feel powerful and I love to learn English.

Another reason being bilingual is important to me is so my family and I feel comfortable here in the U.S. If we can speak English, we can take care of ourselves. For example, one time we went to a store and my mom needed a bracelet, but I didn't know that word. We had to go to a lot of places to find it because I could not ask for help. Sometimes my parents need me to be a translator for them because of language. We can enjoy some benefits if we can read and speak English. For example, we can read newspapers or magazines to learn about what jobs are good for us, and know how to apply for them, how to fill out the application, and how to interview. Being bilingual makes me feel that we belong here.

Learning culture is also an important part of being bilingual. In Vietnam we have a different calendar to welcome the New Year. Usually, our calendar is a month behind the American calendar. So when my family moved here, we had two New Year's Eves for each year. I already knew what Thanksgiving Day was when I came here. This is a great celebration that I did not have in my country. When I go back to my country to visit, I will share about the culture here. Because of being bilingual, I am learning not only the language, but also the American culture.

I realize that being bilingual is very important to me because I need to communicate with other people. My family feels safe when we live here, and so I can learn more about American culture. Writing down these words is an example of my achievement in learning English. I definitely will never really be able to say thank you to all who have helped me. At Health Sciences and Human Services High School, my teachers and my friends are wonderful and they help me learn English. I still don't feel confident communicating, but one day I will. With my ability, I'll be able to do more in life. When I first came to the U.S., I went to the Secondary Bilingual Orientation Center School. There was a quote on the wall there that said, "You never know what you can do until you try to do it." I will always believe that.

 **ARTHUR BRADFORD** is the author of *Dogwalker* (Knopf) and *Benny's Brigade* (McSweeney's). He is also the director of the "How's Your News?" documentary series and most recently the Emmy-nominated film "Six Days Air," about the making of South Park. He lives in Portland, Oregon.

THE POND

If you followed the dirt road into the woods you would see that it faded away into a grass covered path. And if you followed that path through the trees and down a small hill you would find a pond. When I first saw that pond I didn't think much of it. It was just a bean-shaped body of water about as wide around as your average house, maybe a little bigger. It was a hot summer day and I considered taking a swim there but the farmer who owned the land had warned me against it.

"You never know what's brewing in a still little pond like that," he had told me.

When I stepped closer to the pond a number of tiny frogs leapt from the shore and into the water. I watched them swim to the sandy bottom and noticed then that this pond was quite deep. It must have been fed by a steady spring because there was no algae or green scum along the sides.

Most ponds that size turn to swamps in short order, but this one here seemed destined to remain a fine clear pond forever. I peered out towards the center and I couldn't even see the bottom. That's how deep it was.

So I decided to ignore the farmer's warning and take a little dip. I removed my clothes, all of them, because I was in remote territory, and I slowly waded in. The frogs on the shoreline erupted in a chorus of peeps. As I waded in deeper the peeps grew louder and louder until I had to cover my ears. The water felt cool and refreshing though and I let my body fall in and took a few strokes towards the middle. It was a pleasant experience, except for the frogs. By the time I was finished with the swim and stood drying myself on the shore, the peeping had become ridiculous.

"PEEP! PEEP!"

"I was just taking a swim," I called out to them as I put on my clothes. But they couldn't have heard me above all that racket. I waved good-bye to the small pond and walked back along the grass path to the dirt road.

It was several days later that I noticed something unusual. There was a green fungus growing between my toes. Fungus in the toes in not particularly unusual, but green fungus is. Each time I cleaned it off, the fungus would quickly return.

Later I noticed that this green substance was building up between my fingers as well. It had a damp, musty odor, like that pond, and I now regretted ignoring the farmer's warning and taking that dip when I had.

That night, as I slept, I had a funny dream about the pond. I was back there swimming and those frogs were chirping and I was asking them to be quiet when a large head popped out of the water. I say "large" but it was no bigger than my own head. The reason it appeared large was because it was the head of a frog. It had two enormous glassy eyes and they gazed across the water's surface at me.

"Hello," I said to the frog.

The big frog replied, in a beautiful, sing-song, feminine voice, "Hello there stranger..."

It was at that point that I woke up. I was distressed to see that between my toes and fingers, where the green fungus had been, there was now a thin layer of skin. Overnight, I'd grown webbed feet and hands. My body began to itch as well and my skin felt dry and cracked. I went to the bathroom and poured water upon myself and this seemed to help, though I was disturbed now by the slimy quality of my skin. It addition to the strange texture, it had also turned a shade of pale green. I took heavy, panicked breaths and paced about the room on my floppy webbed feet trying to figure out what to do.

The distant peeping of those frogs began to ring in my ears. I slapped myself a few times with my long webbed fingers to see if I was still inside of that dream, but I did not wake up.

Instead I found myself outside, back on the dirt road, taking long hop-like steps toward that odd little pond. It was dawn when I finally reached it, and a fine mist hovered over the water's surface. As soon as I stepped out of the woods the frogs began to sing.

"Peep! Peep!" they called out.

My skin felt awfully dry at this point so I slipped once again into the cool water. It felt very good, more refreshing than any swim I'd ever taken. My webbed feet and hands were particularly adept at propelling me along and I dove down into the cool water's depths. When I opened my eyes things were surprisingly clear. I could see small fish scurry away and the other frogs paddling about around me. I stayed under for a long spell and found no desire to come up for air.

"This is not so bad," I thought.

And then, down below, I saw her shape. She swam up my way and there before me sat floating the most beautiful frog I had ever seen. Her bulbous eyes peered out at me with a wondrous swell of understanding. She seemed to know and comprehend every thought and emotion I was feeling. We swam around each other in graceful circles, our long sinewy legs brushing against each other in the murky depths.

I heard that sing-song voice again, melodious unlike any other.

"Stay with me," she said, "We'll inhabit this pond together. In the winter we'll sleep peacefully under thick clear ice, and in the spring we'll make thousands of little eggs..."

It was a tempting offer, I told her, but I had business to attend to back above the water's surface. A gaze of sorrow washed over that beautiful frog's face and she sunk back down to the distant depths of the pond.

I hoisted myself up out of the water and hopped back out to the dirt road. The morning sun was now beating down upon me and it felt disagreeable on my skin. Still, I hopped all the way back out to the main road where I flagged down a passing truck. The driver pulled his rig over and I hopped up inside.

"Watch the seat leather," said the driver, "You're getting slime all over it."

"I'm sorry about that," I said.

The driver pulled out a newspaper and I sat on that so as not to ruin the seat.

"Where are you headed?" asked the truck driver.

"Well," I said, "I was going to go home, but now I realize that none of my clothes will fit me. I'm not even sure if I'll enjoy things so much back at home, what with my body being changed the way it is."

"Well," said the truck driver, "you do make for an unusual sight."

We bounced along in his big, tall truck for a while and I watched the trees and houses and cars flash by through the windows.

Finally I said to the driver, "I'd like to ask you a favor."

"What is it?" he said.

"Perhaps you wouldn't mind taking me back up that dirt road, back where you picked me up."

"I wouldn't mind," said the driver, "not for a fellow like yourself."

So he slowed down and turned his big rig around. When we reached the dirt road he turned up it and drove me all the way to the end. Then we walked together through the woods, back to the pond.

When we got there the truck driver said, "You know, I've fished in this pond many times and I've never caught a fish. I've never even had so much as a nibble."

"Maybe that's because of the frogs," I said.

My skin was feeling terribly dry by this time so I bid the truck driver goodbye and slipped back into that cool water. Let me tell you, that pond felt good on my skin. I paddled about in sheer glee.

Later I swam down to the smoky bottom and called out for my pretty lady friend. After much cajoling she came out from under a pile of decaying leaves and stared at me with unblinking eyes.

"I was a fool to leave," I told her. "I want to stay here in this pond with you. We'll nestle together under the winter snows and raise up a pile of little tadpoles."

At first she was unwelcoming of my advances.

"You're too late," she told me. But I persisted.

"I had to make that mistake," I pleaded. "I had to venture out and see what the world held for me. But now I know. You can be sure I'll never leave."

This is the speech you must make to your respective partner after such a foolish errand as mine. It matters not if you are a frog or a human. It took time and faith, but eventually that lovely frog warmed to my advances.

We live together now, at the pond at the end of the road. I imagine you've been there before and hardly given it a thought. You probably noticed the little frogs hoping in off the shore and the tiny tadpoles flickering along the sandy bottom. You probably slapped at some mosquitoes when they pricked your arm and maybe you thought about what else lay underneath the water's surface. I bet you didn't think about us down here together though. And even if you did, I imagine you'd never guess just how happy we are to have found each other in such an unusual place as this.

Photo by Willie Davis

PETER MOUNTFORD'S debut novel, *A Young Man's Guide to Late Capitalism* (Houghton Mifflin) won the 2012 Washington State Book Award and was a finalist for the VCU Cabell First Novel Prize. His short stories and essays have appeared in *The Atlantic Monthly*, *Granta*, *Salon*, *Best New American Voices*, *Boston Review*, and elsewhere. He is a 2012-13 writer-in-residence at the Richard Hugo House in Seattle.

PAWING THE MINK
IN LOS ANGELES

I spent the first eight months of 2004 in Los Angeles selling furniture to rich people. In the center of the store sat a colossal white sofa, extremely uncomfortable, which could be purchased for $8,000. No one bought it. A full set of silverware would set you back something like $15,000. No takers. A mink throw—$7,500—also did not sell. Another mink throw, available for $5,000, actually did sell. In fact, I sold it. My single biggest commission. A frosty rich lady once bought an entire set of handcrafted Italian dishes: my second biggest commission. On the whole, though, I wasn't a very good salesman. I sold lots of tablecloths. Glasses, too. I sold a lot of glasses.

One thing I learned: Rich people like a little pushback. They enter a store acutely aware of their wealth and what it means in this context, and this knowledge, by definition, is tied up with their sense of self-worth, for better or worse. They want you to be serious and professional with them, but they also want you to be able to slap their hand when they go astray. Mostly, they want you to care, even if they're talking about decorative pillows. They want you, in short, to be like Jeeves, or Bruce Wayne's Alfred. They're the boss, sure, but if you're not in control, they'll eat you alive.

"Will this candlestick work with that table?" they'd ask, and I'd sigh wearily. Feigning nonchalance despite my terrifying ignorance, I would not look at them when I talked. With regard to the candlestick, I'd talk to the table itself—explain that it depended on the context, depended on the room. I'd ask questions about the windows, the paint, the ceiling, and then, eventually, I'd pretend to grasp the situation. At that point I'd declare that, yes, the candlestick would work on that table. They'd buy the candlestick, not the table. Of course, if I were a great salesman, I wouldn't have asked questions, would have just demonstrated how such a table only worked with four of those candlesticks, especially when accompanied by certain handmade exquisite napery, etcetera. They'd see a fictitious version of their life, conducted at that particular table, and they'd attempt to acquire it by buying it all. And, as with a great dentist, it'd all happen without them realizing that someone was working on them.

Bridget Fonda, who had married film composer Danny Elfman and had stopped appearing in movies, shopped there compulsively. I have vivid memories of loading cumbersome decorative pots into the trunk of Elfman's Maserati. Zach de La Rocha, the former frontman of Rage Against the Machine, apparently had a lot of time on his hands, too, because he drove his cool Mercedes over all the time and drank coffee by himself at the cafe attached to the store. He looked desperately bored and was always alone. Nicole Richie was not alone when she came to the cafe, nor was Kevin Costner. Victoria Beckham wore her sunglasses indoors, throughout lunch. David Schwimmer came a few times, alone, and was precisely as bitter and patronizing as you'd expect him to be. Gary Oldman was completely banal, just a middle-aged man shopping for furniture with his impossibly gorgeous twenty-something lady friend.

Sharon Stone was bitchy and magnificent, a bombshell even without her makeup. I liked her sass. Unfortunately, when she came in I was wearing my apron. We were supposed to wear these short black aprons, but sometimes they were more humiliating than other times. She was there to buy a Missoni bathrobe for someone and she kept trying to tell me that this guy was a titanic, an ogre. He was like the yeti, but bigger. We had an XXXL robe, but she still wasn't convinced it was big enough. I'm 6-foot-2, built like Zach Galifianakis, but when I put the robe on for her and stood on my tippy toes, she just winced, told me he was at least twice my size.

Eventually, she gave in and bought the robe, plus several $250 coral-encrusted pillows.

The brittle-thin and very short character actress Linda Hunt—you'd recognize her if you saw her, she's everywhere on TV, often with a prominent spot on unmemorable shows like *NCIS Los Angeles*—entered with her wife, who resembles Joan Didion. Hunt might have been the most appealing person I met that whole year in Los Angeles. She was grandmotherly, hilarious and familiar, even a little flirtatious as she chided me for trying to upsell her into buying a pair of $450 wicker chairs. Still, she wavered—she loved the chairs, really loved them, but she kept doubting herself, saying they were too big for someone her size. Then she'd acknowledge, with help from her wife, that the chairs would probably be used mainly by other normal-sized people. In the end, I think she said something to the effect of, "I'm sorry, I know it'd be a good commission for you, but I just can't do it," and left empty-handed. She never learned my name, but she talked to me like I was a human being, like we were both human beings. When she left, I wanted to chase her out and buy her a beer.

Most people, learning that I was a writer, assumed I wrote screenplays and would give me their cards, begin talking about their film projects. I'd have to explain that I wrote for the page, for reading. At which point they would halt, midstream, and gaze at me with delight, like I was some charming curio in an antique shop, a lovely anachronism. Then they would walk away.

Jennifer Lopez didn't ask me what I did outside of the furniture store, fortunately. She was pleasant enough, but her then-fiancée, Marc Anthony, stood to the side, glowering, and I was immediately possessed by a visceral hatred for him. She wore a white hat pulled down low on her head to prevent people from recognizing her, but when she leaned across the counter and locked eyes with me and I realized who she was and then briefly and involuntarily gawked at her, mouth ajar, she smiled sweetly, no doubt accustomed to stunned shopkeepers. You hope you'd remember that these people are just people, after all, people who have to floss and deal with bad traffic, who wear uncomfortable shoes and regret it, but then they're in front of you all of a sudden asking you questions and it slips your mind. Like so much in Los Angeles, it's humiliating. Lopez walked around the store and I followed, hypnotized by the pendulum swings of her hips. What I thought to myself was: I am looking at Jennifer Lopez's ass. That was the depth of my insight.

She told me that she wanted many, many dainty English teacups. But our dainty English teacups weren't quite dainty enough. Instead she bought fifty napkin rings. Or, she picked them out and Marc Anthony paid for them. He had a black American Express card, which signifies an ominous degree of wealth, and, looking at it, I noticed that his name was not "Marc Anthony" at all. He had a string of names and none of them were "Marc" or "Anthony."

A week later, the two of them were married in a small ceremony with about fifty guests. Then the napkin rings made sense.

A week before her divorce from John Stamos became public information, Rebecca Romijn-Stamos entered five minutes before closing with a tall gay man who wore comically long and pointy shoes. I didn't recognize her. It'd been a long day, a long six months in Los Angeles, and I was deeply tired. The two of them were fondling the $5,000 mink throw, as so many people did, so I flatly asked if they wanted me to put it on hold for them. That was usually how I scared people away from the blanket. But she said yes, she wanted it to be put on hold. This struck me as nonsense, because no one wanted a $5,000 mink throw. So I handed her a yellow HOLD card and a pen and said that if she put her name and number on the card, I'd attach it to the blanket and I'd call if someone else made a move for it in the next couple days.

Then I went back to counting my till.

She started writing and then stopped, looked up at me, and said, "Wait, you're going to leave this card out here? I'm not going to write my number on it."

I put the money down, looked back at her. It took a couple more seconds before I realized who she was. I told her I'd hold the blanket for one day without the hold card. Then I gave her a business card with my name on it and said if she still wanted the blanket tomorrow, she could call me. As a teenager, I had scrutinized her airbrushed body in Victoria's Secret catalogs, but when she'd stood right in front of me, I had no idea who she was.

The next day, I answered the phone and Rebecca Romijn-Stamos asked for me. By name. "I've decided to take it," she said.

"Okay," I said, and imagined her lying on the throw. Then I thought about all the many hands I had seen fondling the blanket before.

She picked it up the following day, without the aid of her clown-shoed decorator. I had wrapped it up and placed it in a huge bag, which I passed to her once I'd run her credit card and taken a duplicate. A couple of days later, her publicist announced that she and John Stamos were getting a divorce. Then the mink throw made sense.

Personally, I wanted everything in the store. I wanted the objects and I wanted the people. I wanted to eat them all up, gnaw on their bones. At first, I didn't care about it all, thought it a lot of silliness, but soon enough I was fantasizing, actively, daily, about owning those gorgeous Italian wine glasses, $50 each, and about the house where I'd put my immense and uncomfortable sofa. I imagined the parties on my private beach, shaded by the French marquee that no one else in L.A. owned. Or, no one except Bridget Fonda.

While driving home to the apartment I shared with two roommates in Silverlake, I'd pick out the famous guests that would come to my beachfront house, pictured myself drinking a martini in the setting sun as the sea breeze rippled through my white suit. These things had never seemed relevant before. Now, I felt mortified by my sensible late '90s Volvo, my cheap cellphone. Somewhere nearby, someone was sharing a platter of immaculate sushi with Sarah Michelle Gellar, who's a year younger than me and prettier in person, while I was consuming starchy blocks of Trader Joe's faux-sushi. What I needed, evidently, was a Maserati, a beachfront house in Malibu. What I needed was a better pair of sunglasses, and a life appropriate to those glasses. Until then, I was not alive, I was auditioning for life.

Updike wrote, "Celebrity is a mask that eats into the face," but after living in L.A. for a while, the proper reply became obvious: With a mask like that, who needs a face?

In late August, I quit my job and packed my worldly possessions into my sedan and drove north for Seattle, where I still live. The AC was broken and it was at least 115 degrees in the plains of central California. The wind didn't cool me down, just turned my car into a convection oven, but I dared not close the windows. Stereo all the way up, I locked in the cruise control at 25 miles an hour above the speed limit. And while I did, officially, ride off into the sunset in the end, there was—I'm glad to report—no epiphany, no heart-pounding climax. Like some great shimmering mirage, the entire fantasy merely evaporated from view. I wasn't even out of California before it was gone.

100(ISH) WORD MEMOIR

Flash nonfiction autobiographies

Imagine you've been asked to write your life story—all the joys and pains, delights and anxieties, victories and defeats. There's a catch, though: you must distill your life into 100 words, a flash autobiography that could convey the lovely, intricate, complicated person that is *you*.

Last summer, a group of high school students accepted the challenge of using few words to convey great depth. Of course, their first question was: "Why only 100 words?" While the number is somewhat arbitrary, the enforced brevity pushed our participants to focus on each word as a choice; they became savvier writers as they employed new techniques, style, and richer vocabulary, and made each word earn its place in their life stories. Plus, practicing flash nonfiction exercises that teased out the most influential people, places, and events in their lives enabled students to examine those experiences that had the most impact.

By the end of the workshop, each participant had whittled down their memoirs to roughly 100 words. (We did allow a *little* cheating.) Some focused on one-time adventures or moments of great personal development, while others crafted metaphorical mosaics that patched together rich images that collectively conveyed identity. The trip across continents, the loving touch of a parent, the carefully crafted meal: these brief moments were artfully depicted to represent the magnitude of their influence on the writers' development.

In the end, our writers learned more about their values and selves based on what they chose to highlight. They learned about the pliability and texture of language. And—as evidenced by the pieces they produced—they learned that quality and quantity are not synonymous.

CECE ROSENMAN is fourteen and goes to Mercer Island High School. She plays both the clarinet and the saxophone. When it rains, she enjoys either staying in her room and reading, or going for a cross-country run.

APOLOGIES

1950s cars lining dirty streets. Couples learning to waltz on the sidewalk. Market stalls filled with handmade rag dolls. While I studied the sights, the Cuban people studied me. In an elevator, a young man aimed his camera phone at me. He was so shocked by my pale skin and light hair that he snapped pictures. Laughing, the guy told me to stick out my tongue. I smiled instead. Then, I didn't realize how inappropriate the man's actions were. The man realized and apologized to me as I left the elevator. It was strange when this man, who was starving because of the U.S. trade embargo, was apologizing to me.

ESA TILIJA is fifteen and goes to University Prep. She has eight hens, plays the classical guitar, and has climbed the Gulkana Glacier in Alaska. When it rains, she likes to eat pho at her favorite Seattle restaurant, Pho Bac, and spend time with her friends on cozy couches, eating snacks and sharing stories.

THE LITTLE THINGS IN LIFE

I entered the world as a black-haired baby, my loved ones' hard hands dipped in oil, softly massaging my back.

My two-year-old self, face tinted by slushy bits of watermelon, flying from Nepal to Seattle. I grew up riding bicycles with neighbors, being lured in by dinner spices, and falling asleep to rain's pitter-patter.

My tween self enjoyed my lovely new home where I harvested vegetables, filled my pointy, woven basket with eggs, heard guitar strings wavering in and out of tune, and stuffed the tiny car with camping gear.

By the time I turned fifteen, I felt happy.

Although I am not walking on the same ground that I walked on as a toddler, my mind is peaceful and my heart is strong. My body could be anywhere in the world. It is where my heart and mind are that matters.

 **EDITH MARTINEZ BRINGAS** is sixteen and goes to Shorewood High School. She was inspired to write this piece by her love for her mother, Romalda Bringas Gonzalez. When she's not writing, Edith enjoys doing puzzles, listening to the music of composer Andre Rieu, and spending time in her school library.

MY MOM IS THE WORLD TO ME

My mother is a mature lioness and I am a cub. She demonstrates her love through food.

"Edith, come and eat!" are words describing how much she cares about me. Her working hands are clouds, and as the TV talks she serves me chilaquiles.

After two hours of homework I am the last one to eat dinner, placing the spoon in my mouth with the delicious food becoming an award, along with the beautiful smile my mom gives me. I eat the warm, tasty sensibility that is my mom.

I am reminded of the love she feels for me.

KATHLEEN SANTARELLI is fifteen years old and goes to Garfield High School. She has taken circus classes with her family for the past five years, and also knows how to wire-walk. On rainy days, she enjoys studying Latin, reading historical fiction such as the Lady Grace mysteries, and drinking hot chocolate.

ALL-AMERICAN GIRL

I am walking into the scent of paper, ink, and old leather;

lying in bed hearing stories of my mother's childhood;

limping back to the tightwire, pain shooting down my leg;

singing along with *Top Hat*, wishing *I* could wear Ginger's beautiful ball gown;

anticipating the Seattle skyline that I see every time I come home;

picking purple grapes and letting the sweet, tart taste burst on my tongue;

composing a lengthy letter to Elizabeth on simple white stationery;

praying through dance, my white dress flowing as I twirl through Creation;

I am a laughing, dreaming, romance-addicted, All-American girl.

PETER ROCK is the author of six or seven novels, most recently *The Shelter Cycle* and *My Abandonment,* and a collection of stories, *The Unsettling.* He is at work on many projects and lives with his wife and two fierce young daughters in Portland, Oregon.

SHAKEN

For Motoko Vining

Asada locks his car and turns away, leaving it parked on the shoulder of the highway. He crosses the low ditch and begins climbing upward, following a stream. It's early autumn; these days, the sun stays low and cool, rolling along the horizon for hours. Most of the leaves on the ground are last year's-dried and bleached out, the same dull white as bones.

Walking under the trees, he breathes in, then exhales, the air cool in his throat. He has a sweater tied around his waist, a canteen on his hip, an energy bar in his pocket. In his hands, he carries only his fishing pole.

A year ago was the first, the only time that he'd been to this place. An engineer where he works told him it resembled Japan, and that drew Asada here, stirred his curiosity. His family had moved to the States when he was fourteen, and now he is forty-four; while he doesn't recognize the similarity in this landscape, he hopes it might startle memories from inside him. He has put off his return all spring, all summer. He had to come before his hesitation stretched out into the first snowfall, before the trip was delayed into next year.

His breathing is already coming faster; he slows, but does not stop. This slope climbs for miles, even beyond the timberline, far beyond his destination. He is hiking to where an old stone mill, gutted and abandoned, sits beside the stream, where the remnants of a dam still collect a shallow pool. The stillness there is only disturbed by the gentle slapping of leaves; aspens circle the water.

The year before, standing beside the pool, he had seen what he believed was a shadow on the stone wall of the mill. It folded, though, then spread, and he could not see what might have cast it. Climbing along the wall, twisting higher, the shadow moved as if it held weight and was expanding, growing arms and legs. Asada's chest had gone cold. He had fled down the mountainside, stumbling, not looking back. This time, he won't run. He'll stay. He has not been surprised for a very long time, and he feels a desire to be shaken.

The bank is rough and torn where, months ago, the swollen stream ran. He crosses the stream, trying to follow the clearest path, and fish dart from stone to stone, abandoning the shadows along the edges. Bending, he tightens the laces of his leather boat shoes, the most casual footwear he owns. He wonders if this would be easier with hiking boots, and whether people often hike alone. Perhaps it's usually done in groups, or in couples. He tries to imagine a woman walking beside him.

There is a movement in his peripheral vision, to his right. A deer, standing only twenty feet away, raises its head and stares. It's a doe, slightly darker than the leaves on the ground, ears out like funnels, light showing through them so Asada can see the red veins forking there. He can smell her, also, sweet and rank, tight in his nostrils. Lifting his fishing pole, he points it like a gun; the cork grip presses against his cheek as he sights down the round, metal ferrules, straight at the deer. She only snorts at him, unimpressed. She walks away slowly, her white tail switching back and forth.

Asada also walks on, in the other direction. He is disappointed in the deer for not running, and in himself, somehow, for not making her afraid. This is not a marked trail; he is probably the only person for miles. He wonders how she became so accustomed to people.

Again, as he climbs, he thinks of women. At the computer company where he works, there are several he's friendly with, yet the ones he's pursued have rarely wanted to know him better. White women realize he's not as exotic as he looks, while Japanese women consider him slow to assimilate, to adapt to life in the States. None of these women work in his department, so they cannot understand, cannot know how it affects a person, translating technical correspondence. He uses Japanese words that most Japanese would not know, English words that Americans would never encounter. Together, these two groups of words are like a third language—one beset by redundancy, with two words for every single thing, with almost no one to share it.

Tree branches cross like latticework overhead. He holds his fishing pole in front of him, clearing spiderwebs. Today, he doesn't mind being by himself. He doesn't want to explain his expectations to anyone and, besides, he feels things are more likely to happen if he's alone. The bushes thicken. Parting them with his hands, he looks down just in time to avoid stepping on a dead bird. A crow or raven, its black feathers still shiny while its dull eyes stare. Asada holds his breath. After a moment, he hears a car on the highway, distant now, somewhere below. He leaves the dead bird behind.

He has been walking under the trees, in the shadows, for over an hour when he steps into the clearing. The side of the mill facing the pool is lit by the sun. The white stone wall looks cold and bright; the three windows—two low, one above—are squares of darkness. For a moment, it seems that the mill has moved closer to the water, and then he realizes it's the breadth of the pool that's changed.

The pool is all reflections. The tips of the aspens bend inward, stretching there. Birds dart low across the surface, doubling in the water, folding their wings to plummet, opening them to rise. Asada stands near the low dam, where all the earth has been washed from between the white stones. He looks into the mottled gray trunks of the aspens, at their bright yellow leaves in the sun. Behind the mill, a broken fence stretches, wooden rails down in some places; farther along, a whole section has collapsed.

He notices that there's no lure on the end of his line, not even a hook. It doesn't matter. He casts out his bare leader and the pool ripples and settles. Little trout rise, curious, holding themselves steady in the clear water. He watches until they lose interest, and then he reels in the line. A breeze rolls down the mountain and the aspens' leaves slap and clatter. Asada shivers, sweat drying inside his clothes. His legs and feet are sore from the hike. Then it begins. Ten feet from where he stands, where the pool drops off into slightly deeper water and he can no longer see the bottom. It's as if something is rising from below—an indistinct shape, its edges finding clarity, different shades verging on colors. A round face, almost, a darker body, flickering, trailing off. Asada's heart accelerates, his scalp tightens. A cloud's reflection slides across the pool, blurring the surface, and the image does not return. He looks up, then, toward the mill—it seems a dark shape moves in one of the low windows, as if someone was standing there and has slipped behind the wall, beyond where he can see.

Asada unties the sweater from his waist and sets it on the ground, in case he has to move quickly. He reminds himself that he is more curious than afraid. Attempting to appear calm, he again casts out his line; this time, the trout don't even bother to pretend they're interested. He looks away from the pool, squinting into the aspens, the shadows between them. What he thought were natural marks are actually letters, he realizes, initials and words that people have carved into the trunks. Between the stones at his feet, he now notices cigarette butts; they don't appear to be especially old.

The second time the figure rises, the reflection is in a different place—across the pool, nearer the opposite bank, surfacing between the trunks of trees. Asada looks away, at the mill. The lower windows are empty. He looks up, to the window above.

It is the figure of a woman, standing thin and dark. Steady, unmoving, hands held out in front. It is difficult to make out the face's expression, to tell if the features are Asian or otherwise. The long hair is tangled, hanging across the face. The dress is loose, or perhaps it's a kimono; it hangs as if wet. The figure appears to have just climbed out of the water.

And then the window is empty. Asada almost calls out, but he does not. There are rules, he feels; calling out might simplify the situation, and that is not what he desires. Waiting, trying to remain patient, he wonders if someone standing in the trees, somewhere farther up the slope, might cast their image into the pool so it was reflected upward, so it appeared in the window. No, he decides—if that were the case, the figure would have been upside down.

Asada sets his fishing pole on the ground. Wading, tripping through the bushes, breaking low branches in his hands, he heads around the back of the mill. The wooden door has a lock attached to it, but the hasp has been torn from the wall. The bottom of the door is sunken into the ground; he manages to bend the top enough to wedge his way through .

There is no one else inside. Above, there is the sky, no roof at all. There is no remnant of a second floor, either—not even a ledge beneath the upper window, twenty feet above. No place anyone could stand. Asada steps over crushed, faded beer cans, over the ashes of an old fire. A trickle of water enters under one wall, slips away beneath another. Standing at one of the low windows, he looks out across the pond, to where his fishing pole rests, next to his sweater, which is folded on the white stones. He bends his neck and looks up the smooth wall, at the high window. If he wants the figure to return, he decides, it would be best to return outside, to stand where he had been, to concentrate on the pool's reflections. He crosses to the door and forces his way back through.

The air has turned cooler. He puts on his sweater, eats the energy bar, drinks water from his canteen. He holds his fishing pole like a sword, slicing it through the air. Now it is dusk, and the spaces between the aspens are difficult to see; above, the yellow leaves are pale, unlit. Shadows extend darkly across the pond, threatening to seal off all reflection. He wants there to be every chance, but soon he will be unable to see; he'll have to follow the stream through the darkness, its sound, all the way down to where his car waits.

The black shape comes through the water like a seal, cutting smoothly beneath and not quite breaking the surface. No reflections remain, only shadows. Asada looks upward, toward the mill. The figure has returned, and the face is now more distinct; the hair is thrown back, the features clearly Asian. The arms are still held out. The edges of the shoulders begin to shiver, as if the solidity cannot be maintained, as if the whole thing might dissipate, blow away.

And then it begins to climb through the window. Asada expects it to leap into the pool from that height, but it does not. And it does not swing a leg over the sill, but slides through headfirst. As it comes, it changes, turning fluid, seeping beyond itself. Shadowy, it twists like smoke, rolling down the stone wall, leaving wet marks in its wake, loosing tentacles and spinning them back to the center. At the bottom, the mass unfolds, never settling; it slides across the ground, into the thick bushes.

Asada stands, holding his breath. He will not turn his back. He will not run. His ribs flex inside his chest, their cage rattling its hinges. His senses of taste and smell, his touch and hearing and sight, they are all whittled sharp.

In a moment, the head rises above the line of bushes, on the other side of the pool, just visible against the dusk. Wavering, becoming solid, the body appears in sections, as if ascending a hidden flight of stairs. Then, feet still hidden in the underbrush, the figure starts up the slope. The legs seem to move slowly, yet the body slides smoothly along, its speed increasing. As it heads into the trees, the shadows thicken behind it.

Asada steps quickly, his feet kicking the white stones so they skitter across each other and splash into the pool. When he reaches the aspens, he hesitates, then begins running between them, up the slope, in the direction the figure disappeared. His fishing pole rattles through low branches, snaps in half across a tree trunk; he stumbles, drops it, the line tangling and snapping, the whole thing dragging behind him and finally letting go.

He arrives in a clearing, the ground still slanted, where trees have fallen. Rotten and hollowed trunks cross each other; dried grass pokes up between them. Asada feels that he is close. He breathes deeply, bending over, his hands on his knees. And then, inside a round knothole of one of the fallen trees, he sees what looks like fabric. Dark and wrinkled, yet not a shadow.

He steps closer, and pushes his finger gently through the knothole. As soon as he touches the cloth, a high-pitched screaming sounds from the fallen tree. Asada stumbles backward, falling to the ground. The quiet returns, and yet, through it, there is the faint sound of scratching, of movements within the log. Asada stands, and moves carefully to the hollow end. He squints against the falling darkness.

In a moment, a tangle of black hair begins to emerge. It is a girl, he realizes, a young woman. Loose bark falls from her hair; there's dirt smudged on the pale skin of her face. Her features are delicate, beautiful. Slowly, she crawls from the log and stands, five feet from Asada. Her kimono is soaking wet, and so long it hides her feet. She brushes her hair from her face with long, pale fingers, and tries to smile; her expression is frightened.

"Tadasu-san," she says, her voice low and melodious. "Watashi ga dareka wakaranai no ne?"

"No, I don't recognize you," he says.

"Tadasu-san ga nihon wo detekara sanju-nen mo tatsu mono ne."

"Thirty years?" Asada hesitates, realizing that he is answering her in English. It is the language that comes first to him; she seems to understand.

"Why did you run away?" he says. "Who are you?"

"Sugu ni koe wo kakerare nakkatta," she says. "Tadasu-san ni watashi no iukoto ga wakatte moraenai to omotta no."

"You were right," he says. "I don't understand."

"Yumi yo," she says. "Itoko no."

"Why did you come to me?" he says, but she does not answer him, not right away. Instead, she begins to tell him her story. It has been thirty years since he's seen his cousin, Yumi, and then she was a baby. That was in Japan; she stayed behind, and she is still there, she tells him now. Her body is there, but it is in a place where no one will ever find it. It is in a forest, far from any town, where no one would expect her to be. She rests in a shallow ravine, and leaves have settled on her, icy floodwaters have washed her clean. Over a year has passed since she died. Silt has thickened around her; roots have taken hold, grown straight through her. It is wonderful.

As she talks, Asada watches her carefully, trying to understand. Her voice is like a song, surrounding him, like nothing he's ever heard. He wants to reach out and touch her, but he doesn't dare; he fears she'll sink into the ground, or rise and dissipate through the trees' branches. When he'd stuck his finger through the knothole, her body felt solid. Pieces of bark still hang from her hair.

She is saying that no one in Japan knows that she is missing. She had fallen out of contact with her family—she is ashamed to tell him the details, not that they matter. She is happy now.

"Why did you come to me?" he says again.

"Anata ga watashi ni tottemo aitagatteta kara," she says.

Asada believes this—she has shown herself to him because he had wanted to see her, had needed it, more than anyone else. And he does not pull away when Yumi steps closer. As she leans against him, there is no sound, no change in sensation. The only light is from the moon. Asada turns a slow circle, his eyes searching in every direction. His arms close around himself. He is alone.

ELI ARAO is twelve, and he wrote this story in an 826 Seattle workshop on time travel. One time he ran a challenge obstacle course. He also has been to California. In the future, he plans to travel to Hawaii.

HOW I TOOK THE TIME MACHINE BACK IN TIME AND SAVED MODERN TECHNOLOGY

One sunny day Michael Faraday was walking down Bowmont Avenue to the bookstore to get Isaac Watts' book, *The Improvement Of The Mind*. But when he got there, the book was sold out. Suddenly, he saw a book that looked interesting called *Rameu's Nephew*. So he checked it out and put it in his bag. Little did he know the decision he made would alter history.

Meanwhile, back in present time at the Central Bureau of Time Travel, suddenly the room went dark and everything electronic shut down. The agents knew something was wrong. After lighting many individual candles, they flipped through their history books searching for the cause of the lack of electricity. There were smudges where Michael Faraday's work would be. Instead of the regular work, it said Michael Faraday got the wrong book. So the commander decided to send someone back in time to fix the problem.

And that someone was me. So I gathered up my gear and got into the time machine as the scientists pressed buttons and pulled levers. A big puff of smoke came out. They didn't have enough power. They had a puny bit, but not enough. After thinking for a long time, one scientist had an idea. Quickly, he ran out the door and into the street. A moment later he came back pulling a bicycle and was followed by an angry bicycle rider. Quickly the scientist explained his predicament and the bicyclist agreed to help. Then all the scientists hooked up his bicycle to the machine. The bicyclist started frantically pedaling at the scientist's command. Slowly, the lights started to come on. I could hear the whirring of the time machine's motor. I was going back ten minutes before the incident to switch the books.

Then, there was a flash of light and I appeared in an abandoned shed by the bookshop. The tool shed floor was covered with old rusty tools and smelled musty. I punched in my password for my GPL (Global Person Locater). The password was my name, which is Alex. Instantly, a small blip appeared on my screen and I noticed I was running low on battery. If the battery ran out before Michael Faraday was found, I would lose my way of finding Michael and his only connection to the present. For the next ten minutes I waited, thinking of what to do.

I heard the shop door open, so I peered around the door to see what was happening. Michael Faraday was checking out the book. As he walked out of the shop, I crept behind him and quickly switched the books. Then I went into the shed and went back to 2011. When I got back, all the lights were back on and working. Then the agents had a celebration. We had a gigantic cake with a flashing light bulb on top of it. While I was eating cake my boss came up and patted me on the back and said, "You've saved modern day technology again, Alex. I'm going to give you a promotion." And that's how I saved electricity.

BARBIE FERRER is eleven and goes to Madrona Elementary in Highline. She wrote this piece as part of an in-schools project with 826 Seattle inspired by the book *Seedfolks*. Her biggest adventure was taking a nature walk through her neighborhood, where she found spiders and lizards. In the future, she will write many more thrilling stories.

AMELIA

I was surprised when my dad said we were moving to America. I remember the night my father told me. I had come out of my bedroom and walked into the kitchen, snooping for a snack. When I saw my dad looking at the bills, his face was red as a tomato. He sighed. I went to the living room.

"What are you doing, Tommy?" I said to my little brother. He was watching cartoons.

"I'm watching 'Tom and Jerry,'" he said.

I sat down with him on the floor. Before I knew it, it was 9:32 pm—past Tommy's usual bedtime. All of a sudden my dad barged into the living room.

"We're moving to Cleveland," he barked. "It's too expensive here. We need to meet some new friends."

I was stunned. *But Canada's my home. I don't want to leave*, I thought. The next week, we boarded the plane. We had to leave Nathan, my big brother, because he was going to college to be a policeman.

When we arrived in Cleveland, we went to our new apartment. I saw black, dull carpet on the floor. It smelled musty. I went to my new room. I saw a lamp, an old bed, and a closet full of dust.

I went outside and walked down the street to a park to try to make friends. The other kids thought I was strange.

"Where are *you* from?" a tall girl said. "You talk weird!" Because I was French Canadian, I spoke English with an accent. I just walked away, feeling a little bit depressed, and went back inside to my bed to fall asleep.

The next day, I felt a cold breeze on my face. It woke me up from dozing. As I got up, I went to our new kitchen and grabbed some Frosted Flakes. My dad came in.

"After breakfast we're going to the community garden," my dad told me. "I read about the garden in the paper. We could grow and sell and eat some vegetables there." I nodded, half asleep.

The garden was nearby on a street, right by the sidewalk. There was a wooden fence surrounding the garden, with apartments beside it. There were rows and rows of plants, and lots of small plots. It was full of people of all ages—some kids, some teenagers, and lots of adults. People were speaking different languages. No one was making fun of how people talked. I felt like I could be myself.

Once we were in the garden, I looked to my right and saw a young boy working next to an old man, raising plants and planting seeds. The old man called him Gonzalo. I decided to help them.

After I helped, I saw an older girl. She had black hair and blue eyes.

"What's your name?" I asked her.

"My name is Kimberly."

She went to the high school by my middle school. We became friends.

At least I have one friend, I thought to myself.

It took a long time for the plants to grow.

"It's been six months, Dad, they're wilting," I said one day.

My friend, Kimberly, came over to help. She helped save our plants. In four days, they had grown tall. My dad was so happy. We danced and sang and thanked Kimberly. The next week, we sold our plants. At night, I fell asleep and dreamed I had lots of friends.

After a while, I became happy in Cleveland with new friends. Two weeks later, my brother, Nathan, came to visit while he was on summer vacation. My little brother, Tommy, was very happy to see him. Nathan played with him all day. Later that day, Kimberly came over to meet him. We all went to the garden to look at the plants. I decided I liked Cleveland. It was home.

 **JARED LEISING** is the author of a chap-book of poems, *The Widows and Orphans of Winesburg, Ohio,* and a long-time volunteer for 826 Seattle. Before moving to Seattle, Jared received his M.F.A. in Creative Writing from the University of Houston, and in 2010, he curated the Jack Straw Writers Program. He teaches English at Cascadia Community College in Bothell, Washington.

THREE PIECES

SINGAPORE PROMENADE

Bats dive and glide, but lizards stick like chocolate
commas to the sides of this milky high-rise hotel.

They take pause, slip past open windows, and steal
sleep in cobalt kitchen shadows—like our hoboes

in their hallowed boxcars. I wonder how
I'd look twenty-seven stories down: if I jumped

or was pushed. My cousin's deaf. I'm staring
at her pale, hungry hands as they flicker

behind sliding glass, smudged with a prism of prints
from the cotillion of warm fingers inside

doing all the talking. I can't hear them either; I don't dance.
Instead, I reach out to touch the lid of this

young city: a creamy corsage burns atop the refinery
and I can feel its heat pressing against me.

LIES SING

Got your letter, very clever. You misspelled my name again, this time on purpose leaving no return address, no room to move; the first envelope since my departure. It traveled cross-country, tailing me like an unmarked car through eastern Washington desert, a piece of Idaho, bleak Montana stretches, the Black Hills. In Iowa, I recognized your hand at the wheel—Bic-blue kisses on the seal—your rendition of a frequent flyer, correspondence as passenger, racking up another mile of words.

But you'd acted like there was that much between us long before I left. Passing notes and passing out in that dank Yakima bar. We slid cocktail napkins, bloodied with ink, black and forth across the table's radius, stabbing at each other with a felt tip, gin and tonic and I forget, but did we go home together?

I'm sorry I've waited so long and all I do is write you, but it's too late: I'm in Texas, you're overseas. Our differences are well defined by lines. Tabletops have become time zones, and you think fourteen hours in advance *no matter what I do, yesterday and today won't combine in me or you.* Yet, we keep writing. Tomorrow's episode, we're letting our hair grow, learning to smoke and behave like a lady. Dress to impress, now that's depressing.

Don't look now, but I'm turning us into another John Hughes production, call it a gut reaction. You be Molly Ringwald and I'll keep coating us with sweet half-truths (a thin white film that gives you more of what you want in me): the dry heaves. I picture you picturing me, bent at the waist, trying to edit the irony of depth—babies drown in just inches of bath water—but you know it's not just love that I feel for you; it's a song.

THE SENIOR CENTER
Arapahoe, Nebraska

They post signs here: in the restrooms, reminding you to flush; in the wide white kitchen, asking you not to take food; and there are children's gates that'll block your passage up and down. Up, there's an indoor archery range turned dance hall turned storage floor.

Imagine being the ghost of an arrow, traveling through the front brick across Main where Dad tells me they used to bowl, shoot pool—but now, it's a vacant lot.

In the center's basement, the ceiling is low, and three pool tables are covered with plastic; grand pieces of aged felt furniture. Grandpa is over six-feet, and down here, he slumps even more as he takes the cover off one green table and chalks up.

On a card table, three black cases are open: cold, beautiful cues, halved in soft, red beds. I take one. He tells me guys don't come down here anymore. "Too tired," he says.

I rack. We play eight-ball, his rules: the one and fifteen go in the side pockets; if you scratch, take your ball out; if you hit one of his balls before hitting your own, you put it down. This man hasn't played in a bar and won't.

He breaks, and I read his name, *Gilbert*, in blue marker on a white board, along with a smudged date indicating when he last sunk the eight on the break.

He makes a stripe; I'm the little ones. There are other names on the board—*Bernard, Marvin, Raymond*—but I've never met these men, just their sticks, still asleep on a table beside us. I take off my sweater. It's my shot.

ART-A-PHONE

The telephone game, reimagined with art and writing

Ekphrasis ('ek*fra*ses) **noun**. A literary description of, or commentary on, a visual work of art.

It's an age-old question—where do writers and artists get ideas? One Friday afternoon, a group of students gathered at 826 Seattle to answer it. The students' task? Draw inspiration from a famous work of art and transform it into words.

The students each looked at a different painting, and focused on a specific element in the work—the ethereal cold and isolation in a Mark Ryden oil painting, or the steely gazes of the women in Frida Kahlo's "Two Fridas"—to inspire an original poem, short story, or narrative.

The student writing was then passed to a different adult artist, who then created an original work of art of his or her own. From there the chain continued. The new art pieces were passed to another group of student writers, and their writing was then given to a final set of adult artists to complete the chain. The result was an impossibly imaginative game of "Art-a-phone" (like the whispered "telephone" party game) that was unveiled and displayed to the public for the spring Greenwood Art Walk Festival. This section showcases a few results.

Of the experience, young 826 author Jasmine said, "Art inspires me to write because I think the interpretation is the most important part of writing. Visual art is open to free and unbounded thought. In that, it is so versatile."

This project epitomizes the essence of the creative process and the goals of 826 Seattle. It is the culmination of a community of creators, young and old, budding poets and future novelists, graphic designers and professional piñata makers, finding inspiration in each other's work and coming together in the creation of original art. Ekphrasis at its finest.

STELLA FRECHETTE is ten and is home-schooled. She is inspired to write by pictures and daydreams, but really, she can find inspiration in just about anything. Her fondest memory is of the first time she ever slow-gated a horse named Reno. In the future, she will be a professional horse trainer and rider.

This writing inspired the art on page page 177 →

TWO WOMEN WITH A VEIN

I was walking through the Frida Kahlo exhibit in the Seattle Art Museum (SAM, for short) when I stumbled upon a painting of two women, one with scissors with blood dripping on her dress. A vein that was attached to her heart followed over to the other woman and attached to her heart.

That very second, a gust of wind blew on the painting and a tunnel formed. So of course I climbed in and began to walk farther and farther and farther until I came upon the end of the tunnel. The tunnel was dark and empty. The farther I went, the more I had the feeling that something was behind me. I looked behind me a couple of times to see that the back of the painting was following me.

So I ran and ran and ran and soon I was in a loud, small village. I sauntered around the neighborhood. There was the scent of fajitas. (A fajita is like a burrito with red peppers, green peppers, orange peppers, onions and—most of all—steak and chicken. All these things are cooked together.) I do not speak Spanish, so it was hard to understand what people were saying. Some cops were eating fajitas, but when they saw me they jumped out of their seats and ran straight toward me. I jumped into action and went into a little house to hide. There were two women sitting down, the same ones I saw in the painting. I stumbled back and fell.

One of the women said, "You poor little girl. What is your name?"

I answered back, "Cops are looking for me and my name is Sara."

"You can hide here. Just go under that table," one said. So I did, just in time.

The cops came in and said, "Maria and Elupita, there is a little girl on the loose. Have you seen her?"

"No."

"No."

"Okay, thank you." The cops left, so I climbed out from under the table.

"Your names must be Maria and Elupita," I said.

"Yes, and we have a favor to ask, if you would do it for us," they said.

"What is it?" I asked.

"Our hearts are attached. Can you grab the scissors and cut the vein that has kept us together?"

"Yes, but why have you not done it yourself?"

"Our arms are paralyzed, and we can't move them."

So I cut the vein and the women thanked me. I snuck through the neighborhood, climbed through the tunnel, and jumped out of the painting. The tunnel disappeared. I started walking away but something caught my eye. The vein was gone from the painting, and the women were smiling.

So I left to go home to ask my dad if dinner was ready. It was. And it was fajitas!

Art by Skylaar Amann

This art inspired the writing on page 179 →

RACHEL WITUS is seventeen and goes to Seattle Academy. In addition to writing, Rachel enjoys painting, drawing, listening to music, and spending time with her corn snake, Napoleon. Her favorite refuge from the rain is the Seattle Art Museum.

← *This writing is in response to the art on page 177*

TWO CRIMSON BEETS

They fought from behind their picture frames
In the light pink room neither agreed on
The safe ground between cloud and sky
The color was chosen for them

If Maria was a pepper, Elupita was an onion
Connected at the chest by a single lovely vegetable root
Would you think those tubers look like the ventricles of a heart?

The girls both knew it but refused to admit
That the string, which attached them, was slender but strong
And though Maria's eyes stung at Elupita's accidental sting
Her bright and thick outer skin saved her flesh from any burn

Elupita did not mean to singe
With her words, smooth truth
Permeated with the flavors of reality sinking in
Maria saw their worth but could not hear their meaning
Elupita tried and Maria cried but neither could ask forgiveness

So into their golden frames they climbed
Mirror images of snow and sea
And though they crossed their arms and turned away
Their hearts—two twin crimson beets—agreed
As long as those eyes remained locked and dark
They would sit in their light pink room
And be

LUCILLE CORBIT is seventeen and goes to the Center School. When it rains, she likes to drink tea, watch Christmas movies, or hang out at her favorite counter table at Diva Espresso. Her favorite thing to read is old journals or letters, and if she could be any animal, she would be a cat.

This writing inspired the art on page page 183 →

HOW TO FALL

If you ever want to fall,
First you have to slip.
Let your limbs become heavy
Heaving breaths before your lips,
Just forget.
Let the day rush past you wave by wave,
Washing stories on your shore
Becoming shallow page by page.

Torn like tulips,
Toss your worries in the air.
Take in salty breaths of calm
in order to prepare.

Make a mess of everything around you,
Because you want to.
Ignore all prior notions of what this could lead to,
Because you need to.
Because it takes every ounce *of* you,
Just to *be* you.

Let your thoughts climb to the top of a tree
And look down.
Cling in silence to the branches
And let the wind make the sounds.

Realize that you've never been so tall,
And that nobody can catch you if you never learn to fall.

Begin to drop with every second.
Adrenaline pumping past your ribs,
Change your angle while departing, leading lightly with your hips.
Don't look down, ensuring safety,
Just allow yourself to live.
Because if you ever want to fall,
First you have to slip.

Art by Sara Ewalt

AVA HALL is nine years old and goes to Adams Elementary. She is inspired to write by ideas that just sometimes come to her mind. One day, she will be a famous illustrator and author.

This writing inspired the art on page 187 →

SNOW PERFECT

I was walking in the cold forest not far from my house when I stopped right by a voice of someone singing. I ran behind a snow covered fir tree right next to me. The voice sounded like a little girl. I was confused. I thought I was the only person who walked around these woods.

I peeked around the tree and saw a little girl with perfect blond hair that looked white when the sun shined down on it. She had big sparking blue eyes and wore a fluffy white dress. She was sitting down on the cleanest white patch of snow in the woods, petting three white squirrels. She was quietly singing a song that went a little like this:

"If you are here, please come, because I love it when you just tell meeee....
Th-uhhhhhh snow is white. Per-fect for playing in, so just tell meeee...."

She sang it over and over again. Then she stopped singing and locked her eyes onto something. She jumped up like she was poked with a sharp pin. She started to walk backwards. She motioned the squirrels to back away. She hid behind the bushes. The thing came closer and closer. It was enormous and was floating in the air like an angel.

I started to run away, but tripped on a tree root. I fell through a hole. Then my whole world went black.

This art inspired the writing on page 189 →

Art by Justin Allen

JASMINE SUN is an eighth grader at Odle Middle School who wishes for a better world full of books, pho, and free WiFi. She would like to say she is an interesting person who engages in interesting hobbies such as making crepes and hula dancing, but she would actually rather spend copious amounts of time on the Internet correcting people's grammar and watching videos on the correct way to pronounce "Uranus."

← This writing is in response to the art on page 187

LUMINOUS

A tentative step forward. The fluorescence was enticing, reaching its wispy tendrils out toward her. Her own life felt like a mess, muddied and a whirlwind of confusion. She shifted her eyes toward the dreamy light. Soft music floated out of the glowing chasm, riding the breeze. The gentle radiance seemed to encompass the rainbow, the gap emitting pale crimson and cerulean hues that painted the world in soft pastel. The light ahead was so beautiful, so amazing, and so *perfect*.

Perfect, unlike the dark times of the past, a perfect contrast from an imperfect world—after all, wasn't that all she wanted? Impulsively, her feet gradually picked up speed, walking, skipping, sprinting towards the light. She didn't know what she expected to find in the luminescence, but she was drawn to the abyss as if pulled by a magnetic force.

The music grew louder and the beat faster, the colors more radiant. Suddenly, her destination became clear—a deep, pitch-black crevice. There was no music. There was no color. The jagged cliff dropped off, disappearing into the dense blackness. She searched the gap for the alluring melodies and the rainbow that had promised her a better life. In the back of her mind she knew there was no magical Garden of Eden, she knew that the enchanted land of beauty was a mirage, a mere illusion. And yet it was impossible to forget the light that danced and lit up the world; she could not throw away that feeling of utter joy and belonging.

The hope that this delusion could become truth was simply too strong, and in the next moment her perception of reality shattered. There was no past and no future, only the decision that remained in the present, and it seemed that the time to contemplate and ponder the choices was down to a couple grains of sand in the hourglass. She turned back, and saw only the deep mire and the twisted branches. She looked ahead, and saw a black hole. Neither option was delectable. Suddenly, she remembered the paradise that had been ahead, and with one final glance at the dark and gloomy forest that lay behind, she grasped the last morsel of hope for anything good that *just might be*.

A tentative step forward—and she was falling.

NASEEM RAKHA is a mother, author, knitter, sewer, and spy. Her greatest talent is sleeping. She can do it anywhere and anytime. She has won awards for her writing and journalism and she keeps them in a box beside her long yellow shelves of National Geographic. She is the author of *The Crying Tree*, a book she dearly loves and is well loved by others. She is working on another novel which she hopes people will love just as well. Naseem paints the inside of her fingernails with turmeric and dirt from her garden.

THE WAY OF WATER

Hope is a boat that will not float.

That is what Abujan just said, and he should know. My father carves boats from the hard core of jackfruit trees; wide-bottomed slips long enough to fit twelve men yet light enough for a single man to pull himself across the lazy waters surrounding our home—dark waters, living, breathing, giving us all we have known, swallowing all we throw in. Except my Abu's boats. They, apparently, never sink.

When I first told Abujan of my hope to float beyond our river world, to continue my studies, to become someone who achieves dreams, he just wagged his head like a loose button, offering neither approval nor disapproval. Not criticism, nor commitment.

But lately I get singsong words warning me to keep my expectations pinned to the ground. I am a sixteen-year-old girl, after all. A dhobi, washing other people's clothes, nothing more. A girl living in a village soaked by legions of dark water.

It doesn't matter that my teacher walked the rutted path to our home, drank chai with my parents, pointed to my papers, my grades, the offer of a scholarship from a college in Kochi. None of this matters, say my parents.

The worst is my mother.

"What use is any of it to you, daughter?" She spits out our relation as if it is a hair caught between her large, horny teeth. *Daughter*, such bad luck. And school? She sees no use in it. There was no school in our village when she was a child. No desks, no books, no teachers to mock her with papers she could never read.

"And for good reason. What has it done but make you want more?

Look around, Meenah. These rice paddies, this river, this water, this is what you have, and this is all you will ever have. *If* you are lucky."

We live in a world surrounded by water. We plant rice, wade the wet fields, pick leeches from our skin. After the sun retreats, we sit beside our mud block homes, cook our dal, sleep. We are people that people from other shores come to look at. Take pictures. They ask, with the help of their guides, how we live as we do.

As if it were a choice.

They do not understand that hoping for anything different means trouble. Just look at Belusela, the irrepressible Untouchable from across the canal. Crazy with dreams, he ignores the rice paddies that grow out his door, ignores the Zamindar as he comes for his grain, ignores the gold-toothed man's wagging finger and fine wide waist that wiggles when he walks beside the fields passing acrid, meat-filled gas.

Belusela ignores all this, though *this*, says my mother, is all there is to see.

And she should know.

She watches from her perch on the porch, weaving spun cords of co-conut coir into mats for boats—floating boats, curved at the helm like the lip of a shoe. She watches as she grinds grain against the smooth river stones and flicks silver fish scales into the water. She is the village gate-keeper, knowing all that goes on, and it is her buck-toothed job to pierce the flimsy skiff on which hope dares float through our village.

"Don't you ever hope?" I want to ask. "Don't you, when you sit at your altar, put your hopes in your prayers? When pushing in the dirt, did you hope I would be a boy? Did you hope for more children? Did you never once hope for the coolness of the monsoon, a good harvest, a fish-eagle breaking first light with its cry?"

I leave my father beside his work and walk the fifteen steps from our home to the water's edge. There, I stand along the muddy bank and sling rags against the rocks. Over and over. *Slap-splash*, *slap-splash*. Without school there is no hope of hope. Abujan is right. My lessons were my rafts, bringing me the possibility of other shores. Without them, there is only this river, these clothes, this endless rhythm of things that need to be done. There is only dark, sinking water.

Belusela comes floating up on a small craft.

"Good day!" His voice is all clip and clatter, crisp and sharp as a rose-apple.

I stop my slapping and look down, though it is not my place. By rights, it is he who should keep his head low. By rights, the dark Dalit should never come near. But Belusela is Belusela more than he is anything else, and in all my years I have never seen him bow. He floats closer. His smile like white stars in a black sky. He has no fear.

Not like me. I am owned by fear. I serve it its breakfast—cold and hard—every morning. Tiptoe around it while it naps. It is my companion each time I sit with Amajan waiting for whatever brittle words decide to break through her bird-like beak.

"I've just come from Kochi," Belusela says. "It's such a fine place, you would not believe. There are boats the length of rice paddies, fishing nets the size of houses, houses the size of whole villages."

I stop my slapping as Belusela's arms stretch wide.

"You really should come see." He drops his hands in his lap and I slam the rag I hold against the rocks, again, then again. I want Belusela gone. Away. He angers me. He makes me sad. He fills my mind with dreams of places I will never see.

"Look here, Meenah. Even the trash in that great city contains treasure." He pulls a magazine from a plastic bag. It's the color of marigolds, and its cover shows a picture of a white mountain. Belusela holds it out like a rare flower. "This is for you."

I step back. *Gifts from Dalits, well....*

"But you must," he says, flitting through the brightly colored pages. "Who else but you will read this to me?"

I weigh his words. Reading to an Untouchable. It would require stealth. It would require caution. It would require a strong face to do such a thing. Strong shoulders pulled straight by a strong back. Strong eyes never wavering from a strong soul.

But there is this magazine, and its pictures, and promise....

That night, while my parents are deep in their dreamless sleeps, I follow Belusela into the forest where wide-leafed plants hold our shadows. In a small clearing he builds a fire, and I unwrap the magazine from a well-cleaned cloth. "National Geographic," I say, tracing my fingers over the letters. Then with the prudence of a wary child, I open it and begin to read the names of the authors, the editors, the photographers, and publisher. I read about cameras and cars and watches that, with a press of a button, can tell you the time in Tokyo, New York, Milan, and other places with names that taste like sweets. And then I begin the stories. Reading each word, poring over each map, each city, each ridge, and river. Night after night, I flush the words into the thick air as Belusela lies on the far side of the flames, poking coals with a stick.

And then, when I finish the last page, I begin again: every story, every description, everything.

I come up on my father while he works.

"So, hope never floats? It never takes people where they want to go. Ever? Are you sure, Abu?"

I pry my father—try my father. "Testing the water," as Belusela would say, practicing his English on my own hungry ears.

But Abujan won't "take the bait" and, instead, continues to rub his newly-finished boat with a mixture of coconut oil and buffalo dung, stinky stuff, but it gives his crafts a tightness and gleam that sets them apart from others. People come all the way from Kochi, even Goa, searching for the man with the unsinkable boats. He is famous for them in a way only a peasant with one blind eye can be, which is to say, in a way that makes no difference whatsoever.

"Never, Meenah," he says. "Hope is a boat that never floats, a bird without wings, a plucked butterfly, all downy body with no way to survive."

He laughs. A bird with no wings, such a probably-improbable thing.

Then his smile drops.

"Your mother will beat you if she sees you with that." He nods toward my hands. The magazine's pages are stained, its binding cracked.

"See what?" Amajan comes from around the house carrying a pot of oil. She sets it down in the fire then sets her eyes on my hands.

"That again? What is it Meenah? What do you dream today? A trip to London maybe? Maybe a visit with the Queen? Have tea perhaps? I'm sure such a cultured woman would love to meet someone like *you*."

I close my hands into themselves, hiding the filthy lines that crease their surface.

"Your hopes," my mother continues, "are a distraction. A bee buzzing in your ear. And while you search for its honey, what *should* be done does not *get* done!" She points with her chin toward a pile of buffalo dung, and I go and scoop up a wet bowlful and set it beside her bucket.

"Just look at Belusela," she says, pointing her beak toward his mildewed hut. "Hoping to build a touring boat, to start an operation even. To take on guests, to feed them, house them. And *he* a *Dalit*! I tell you it will not go, and it will not do! Those dreams of his, it's bad."

I look down at my feet as they attempt to hide in the dirt. I am a disappointment to my Amajan. A bad harvest.

"What good is it, your head in that book?" Amajan stirs her stinking pot. "You will never see those places. You may as well study the surface of the moon."

Above, the naked day-moon lies flat against the afternoon sky, and my mother stands, clucks her tongue against her teeth, and strikes my head back to the ground.

"Ama!" my father scolds. "Enough. Already enough."

Belusela is building a boat. Not like my father's, made slim and narrow for plying nets though the lagoons and canals that link one village to another. Belusela's boat will stand five meters tall and will be as wide as seven of my father's crafts. It will have a cook stove, and a bath, and a room for guests to lounge as they pass the paddy workers and fishermen, bare backs bent toward the sun. It will have a thatched roof, and carved railings, and a large cotton-stuffed bed with muslin netting draped over its posts like a vale.

"It is a grand trade," Belusela has said. People from Europe, Australia, even America will hire him and his boat and he will cook and clean, and navigate its broad beams across Lake Kumarakom, water hyacinth and reeds poking from its shallow shores.

He will catch *pomfret*, and make fish curry limed with lobes of *cocum*, and sweetened with coconut milk. He will stir masala into their chai, and in the evenings, the night sky wide and soft as a Kashmiri shawl, he will tell them the story of how he built his boat from wood and hope.

A path winds between our house and the river and on it comes Belusela, carrying a long plank of sun-sweet wood. It looks heavy and Belusela's muscles are hard under its weight. But still, he smiles his perfect smile, says hello, and then, with the wood still propped on his shoulder, he greets my mother and me as we work the dung-oil. But we say nothing.

Belusela turns to Abujan. "This mahogany," he says, "was part of an old barge."

My father scans the beam with his one good eye.

"It will not work for me, but I thought, Babu, that you could make good use of it."

My father peers sideways at his wife.

Gifts from Dalits, well....

Amajan will have something to say later, that is certain. But for now there is this wood, and this man, and there is more to be said about boats and wood and the things that keep them afloat. And Belusela listens so well.

The Dalit lays the plank on the ground then crouches before my father, careful to make sure their limbs do not touch.

And I, I sit in the shade serving Amajan bowlfuls of dung, my head bent toward the men's words.

I am a pretty girl. I know this because I've heard my parents say so. They've said it like it is a shame. A waste. So much pretty sitting on such hopeless shoulders.

"But," they've said. "What's to be done?"

There is no dowry for a good match. Instead, it is one of the old village men they have arranged for me to marry. One of the tired and grayed rice-paddy keepers, strapped to land he will never own. And I will be his servant, making him his meals, planting and harvesting his rice, then laying down and reaping whatever drops from my womb.

Then, when the rains come, I will pick up our things and move us to higher ground, returning after the floods to sweep away the scavengers: the lizards and snakes that have found refuge in our home. I will rouse the lazy scorpions and crush the tired moths that bat their frayed wings against the mossy walls. I will clear away all the dark things that become stranded when the water recedes.

My father and Belusela sit back on their heels and sketch boats in the dirt. Then Belusela stands and says goodbye to Abujan, thanking him, then thanking him again.

"His boat will be done in a year," my father comments after Belusela is gone. "Maybe less."

"You," Amajan shoots. "You encourage this nonsense? What good can come of it? What good can *ever* come of a Dalit sitting on our ground, touching our land, our things, our lives? All for what? A piece of rotting wood. Eieegh!"

My father's gaze stays with his boat, his arms with the motion of his work.

I rise.

"Where are you going?" Amajan demands.

"To feed the chickens."

She sucks her ragged teeth and nods.

Behind the house, the chickens scratch at the dirt, hoping, I believe, to find some juicy grubs. And the grubs, they are busy doing their grubby work, hoping to live yet another day. There is hope, I think, for the chickens and grubs at least.

And if for them, why not me?

I sit under a coconut tree and open my magazine to a place called Canada. I know each detail on these pages—each street sign, each look on the red-cheeked Canadian faces. There are cities that gleam with light in Canada, and forests the color of orchids. There are mountains and clear lakes and oceans, and something called snow. I touch its cloud-like world and feel a chill of excitement.

Then I hear Amajan.

"That again?" She descends like a hornet. "And, what about the chickens, the eggs, the work? No, not for you. Not for *my* daughter. She has her head in books. She has her eyes on dreams, places, people she will never, ever see." Amajan rips the magazine from my hands and opens it to an advertisement for a car. "I suppose you dream of owning one of these." She points to the crimson Chrysler with the air cooler and electric windows.

"Free Yourself," the words say, and I smile.

"Yessss—" My mother's voice shuts to a whisper. "I see it in you. You want this—a car, fancy clothes. I suppose you want a fancy house too, some servants perhaps? Perhaps you want to live in Kochi, maybe Bombay with all the movie stars? Oh, yes. Your hopes, your dreams. I can *smell* them on you. And do you know what I smell, daughter? Rot. Sadness, ruin, and rot. I tell you this, Meenah. Your hopes will kill you. Sink you as sure as a stone." My mother's lips shake around her teeth like quivering fish as she rips to another page.

"Ama, no. Don't treat it so!"

Amajan's face jerks up, and she rolls my magazine into a rod, lifts it. The strikes fall on my head, my back, my arms, as I reach out to make her stop.

"No more dreaming." She catches my cheek. "Do you understand? No... more...dreams!"

Willful, she has called me. Obstinate and lazy. I am sixteen, I am pretty, I know how to read and write and dream. And not one of these things, she tells me, will serve.

She shakes her head then turns, striding toward the river.

I race forward. "Amajan, please!"

"No! No more books. No more lessons. No more hopes for something you will never, ever have!"

She throws my magazine, and its pages flutter like a bird's wings, then open and flatten against the black water.

"No!" I push by my mother, leap, then immediately and without hesitation, sink. It is the weight of my clothes, I think, struggling with the curtains of cloth. It is the weight of the water, I think, batting against the dark sludge. It is the weight of my hopes, sinking me as sure as a stone. There will be no Canada, no snow or bridges that cross great waters. No school or teachers or books or exams. No cities with treasures just waiting to be found. There is only this silt bottom. These sunken dreams. This foolish girl, born on water that drowns whatever falls in. I close my eyes, stop my battle. Agree to die.

Someone is beside me. Hands, arms pulling up and up. We break through the surface and I gasp and retch. Then I wipe my eyes. My father's smile is riches, his one good eye a jewel. He points. My tiny golden boat swirls around and around, its pages flagging in the breeze. A Kathnak Dancer, waving her flowing skirts.

"It floats, Meenah. Look there. Your hope, it floats."

GABE HONEYCUTT is thirteen and wrote this piece in the Fractured Fairytales workshop at 826 Seattle. His biggest adventure to date was his road trip to the Southwest. His fondest memory is of having his letter to Barack Obama published in the 826 book of advice to the president. In the future, he will be a writer and creative designer of videogames.

FAIRYTALE LANE

I hated my old life back in the USA. I am a writer[1], so naturally I would decide to go to a strange Germanic town called Fairytale Lane. Of course it was in Germany. I should have known—the name was weird enough. I drove in. First thing I noticed was the names of the stores and houses.

The Three Bears Hunting Surplus. 7 Dwarf Spelunking. (I thought about buying a session because of discounts.) I stayed at the Prince Charming Inn (which was not so charming; the housing and maintenance was infested with rats and bad odor). Once there, I listened to one of the peculiar people of this town. His name was Grumpy. He was short and rather, well, grumpy. He and the innkeeper never got along, mostly because of the inn's signature dish called Medish, a mix of oatmeal and leftover meat that caused diarrhea in most townsfolk. Grumpy, who saw me as a fellow grumpy man, decided to tell me about a little incident that happened a week ago...

Snow White, a super model, was on the run from a fashion magazine CEO who wanted her sued. She later told them that the CEO was an ex-super model from the 70's. The seven brothers took her in. They lacked most skills that they needed and spent their money on Thai food and they really needed a good cook. She did the cooking for them. This crazy woman named Wicked had given her poison makeup, and Snow White fell into a coma. A doctor came by and woke her up with CPR. Nobody even knew why it worked, but it did. The two married. I heard this, and responded by getting drunk at the inn's bar.

[1] I wrote as a journalist for my brother's department in Boston. To be honest, I really hated the job. I was prone to drinking.

At the bar I listened to more peoples' issues in this town. The innkeeper, who I failed to mention is named David Prince, had the reputation of being a charming man. He was yelling at one of his workers for being clumsy.

"SIT DOWN! YOU JUST RUIN EVERYTHING!"

I turned around to see beer spilled on the ground.

The man sat down and started to cry.

"What's up with you?" I asked the man.

"I just spill everything they give me and seem to, well, give bad service," he replied.

"What's your name," I asked, "because I am going to have to apologize."

"Jason, and what do you mean?"

I answered that with puking on his shoes.

"YIIIIII!" he screamed and pushed me[2]. He said some very unflattering things and ran off. I wiped the beer from my face.

"He's just skittish," said someone. I turned around and saw a very tall man. He wore a cop's uniform and had a badge that said in German Constable Knight.

"Well, hello there... Knight."

"That man you just regurgitated on has had a very rough week, okay?" Knight said.

"Like what?" I asked. I really wish I had not. Apparently bank robbers had kidnapped Jason after he slept in their shack, after the German real estate agency came and took his house. The robbers kidnapped him and he convinced them to take him on as a helper. He had to steal some tires and other things to keep on living. He tried to sell the things back but somehow just kept on falling down and bruising himself. This happened every time on the way to the fence (a person who sells illegal goods). Finally, he just threw the tires down the hill and ran down.

The robbers let him in and he continued to do white collar crime. But soon the leader was arrested and Jason was made the leader. Jason sold the master thieves out to the local Germanic police and he was cleared of all crimes.

---

[2] While I was known to do stupid things and be able to keep it up for a while, I was not notorious for holding liquor.

"Wow, that is the second most weird story that I heard today," I said.

"You heard more?" Knight asked.

"You have no idea," I responded. If there is one thing I hate, it's cops who ask way too many questions. And I am not writing about how I get into trouble a lot.

When I was at the bar, I did some things that I will not talk about to get kicked out. I saw this rather mean-looking woman picking the house of the couple that runs the Three Bears Hunting Surplus. I watched and saw her eat some of their food and spit some of it out, then go upstairs and start sleeping in their beds. I saw the couple coming home. I stumbled over and said, "There's a person eating and sleeping in your house!"

I heard screams and saw the girl running out. The father had a shotgun and said some very mean things. "Get out of this house, Goldilocks! You have done it this time!" he said.

My brother Jacob, upon hearing my story, responded with this: "Brother Grimm... You did it this time!"

SADA KALBACH is eight years old and goes to The Meridian School. She wrote this piece in 826 Seattle's Fractured Fairytales workshop. Her biggest adventure was her first actual sleepover. Her fondest memory is of the morning of her fifth birthday when she was so excited she ran into her parents' bedroom and woke them up. She is currently submitting a book review to *Stone Soup* magazine. In the future she will be a professional writer.

LITTLE PURPLE RIDING HOOD

Once upon a time, Little Purple Riding Hood got a purple cloak. "Bring fresh veggies to your grandmother, for she is very hurt by her car accident and they will make her feel better," Purple Riding Hood's mother demanded.

"Very well, Mother," Little Purple Riding Hood replied. She did not mind bringing the groceries to her grandmother, because she wanted to spend time with her anyway.

Little Purple was extra strong for her age, and she liked to use a heavy metal basket to carry things in. She filled her basket with carrots, broccoli, squash, and zucchini and skipped to the forest, where there was a major shortcut to Grandmother's house. As she was walking, Little Purple Riding Hood got very tired. She climbed up on a spiky rock to rest and sipped from a jug of water.

Suddenly, the rock moved, and the veggies fell out of her basket. Sliding down the rock, Little Purple Riding Hood saw two roses., then four roses and two dandelions. She picked them all and put them in her basket. But then, she realized the rock was actually the tail of a stegosaurus! He had an evil grin. Little Purple had learned in school that week that a volcano erupted a long time ago and killed all the dinosaurs in the forest. This one must have survived somehow! The stegosaurus gobbled up all the veggies that Little Purple had dropped and then made his way to Grandmother's house.

He lifted up Grandmother's roof with one of his spikes and swallowed Grandmother whole. Little Purple heard a shriek that sounded like Grandmother's high-pitched scream! Running to Grandmother's house, Little Purple whammed the stegosaurus in his belly with her metal basket full of the flowers she had picked.

"Gulp!" The stegosaurus swallowed Little Purple.

Suddenly, Little Purple's mother jumped out from behind a tree. She had been secretly following Little Purple through the dark part of the woods to make sure Little Purple was safe.

"Take that, you dino!" her mother yelled, and then shot him with a gun. As he exploded, Little Purple Riding Hood and Grandmother popped out, covered in leaves and pieces of brick and wood devoured by the dinosaur.

"The stegosaurus ate all of the carrots, broccoli, squash, and zucchini, but I found two dandelions! Little Purple Riding Hood was smart and knew that dandelions were edible. They had a feast of fried dandelions and lived happily ever after.

JONATHAN EVISON is the author of the *New York Times* bestselling novel *West of Here* and *All About Lulu,* which won the Washington State Book Award. In 2009, he was the recipient of a Richard Buckley Fellowship from the Christopher Isherwood Foundation. He lives on an island in western Washington.

WEST OF HERE

In 1889, upon the behest of a public clamoring for adventure, and a press eager to package new discoveries, thirty-four-year-old Arctic explorer, Indian fighter, and rugged individual James Mather was consigned to conquer the last frontier of the Washington Territory, mere days in advance of its statehood. The sum of Mather's orders, as issued by Governor Elisha P. Ferry himself in a champagne toast and roundly endorsed by the expedition's underwriters, were as follows: "Succeed."

The vast uncharted interior of the Olympic Peninsula, between the Strait of Juan de Fuca and the rockbound coast of the Pacific, was ripe for discovery. For centuries the region had fueled speculation among seafarers, and for centuries the rugged obstacles it presented discouraged even the heartiest explorer. Viewed from the strait, as Juan de Fuca allegedly viewed it in 1579, the heart of the peninsula comprised a chaos of snow-clad ranges colliding at odd angles, a bulwark of spiny ridges defending a hulking central range like the jaws of a trap. The high country was marked by gaps so steep and dark that the eye could scarcely penetrate them, and all of this was wrapped tightly about the waist with an impenetrable green blanket of timber.

When viewed from Elliot Bay on a clear day, the leeward side of the Olympics presented another dramatic facade: a sheer wall of basalt inclining suddenly and precipitously from the banks of Hood Canal, stretching some hundred miles along the western horizon, so steep in places that snow would not stick to the face of them. Indeed, the Olympics presented to Seattle no less than a mile-high barrier to the unknown. And by 1889, the unknown was fast becoming a finite concept.

That Mather chose to launch his expedition in the dead of one of the worst winters on record is less a testament to his poor judgment than his determination to be the first in breaching the Olympic wilderness. He was harried from the outset by the fear that someone would beat a trail to his destiny before him, and this fear was not unfounded. Within a year, no fewer than a dozen expeditions would set out to penetrate the Olympic interior.

With little data to support him, Mather selected the narrow Elwha River valley as the point of entry for the party's crossing. The river ran flat and shoal at its mouth, and the wooded bottomlands seemed to offer an inviting path through the foothills and over the divide. Moreover, the proximity of Port Bonita, just east along the strait, would allow the party a base for their operations during the muddy weeks of trailblazing into the foothills.

Mather and his party of five set out from Seattle aboard the steamer *Evangel* on December 7, 1889, fully outfitted for a six-month expedition, though unprepared for the fanfare that greeted them upon their arrival in Port Bonita. Morse Dock was wrapped in silk bunting, with a dozen coronets sounding "The Spanish Cavalier." Men, women, and dirty-faced children formed parallel lines and watched the parade of trunks emerge from the hold and move serpentine through their midst. Mather himself, a bear of a man, crated a sizable trunk on his shoulder, unaided, gritting a bearded smile as he passed through the crowd. At his heels, untethered, came a pair of big fine bear dogs.

Near the end of the line, seeming to Mather out of place, a small native child seized his attention. Boy or girl, Mather was unable to ascertain, but the child, lithe and moonfaced, squinted fiercely with pointed blue eyes as he passed.

When he reached the staging area, Mather hefted his trunk onto the growing pile, and before he'd even ventured to get his bearings, was met by a very pregnant woman, with a very earnest handshake, and a frazzled knot of hair atop her head.

"Mr. Mather, is it?"

"It is. And you are?"

"Eva Lambert of the *Commonwealth Register*."

Mather glanced past her at the muddy hillside and the ragtag assembly of wooden structures riddling the shoreline, then eyed doubtfully the colorful floppy bow dangling from beneath Eva's shirt collar. "A social register? Here?"

"A newspaper, Mr. Mather. The region's *only* newspaper. And not *here*, but *there*, over the hill at the commonwealth."

Mather smiled down at her through his formidable red beard. He snuck a glance at her belly pushed tight against her blouse, then another at her tiny left hand and saw no band adorning it.

Neither look escaped Eva's notice. "No woman, Mr. Mather, should have to wear seven pounds of underwear. Furthermore, marriage is not a career."

Mather beamed his amusement down upon her once more, scratching his big shaggy head. "So, then, no hearth and needles for you, is it?"

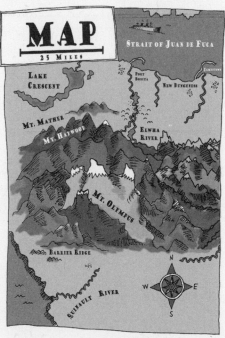

Eva smoothed the cotton blouse over her belly and looked right up into his smiling brown eyes. "It was not my intention to stir your playful side, Mr. Mather. I was hoping to ask you some questions."

Mather could not ignore the heaviness of her breasts but resisted the impulse to look at them. He looked instead at her jawline, sleek in spite of her condition, and the feline complexity of her carriage. "Ah," he said. "You want answers. Well, if that's what you're after, I'm afraid you're out of luck. I've made an exclusive with the *Seattle Press*. They ask the questions."

Art by Nick Belardes

"And who else owns your expedition? Who else has designs on our resources?"

"I'm afraid those are questions, Miss Lambert." He shifted distractedly, removing his elbow from its perch, as another parcel was hefted onto the pile. "Sitka," he called out to one of the bear dogs sniffing among the crowd. The dog came zigzagging back and planted herself at his heels, whereupon Mather rested a huge hand on her head and left it there.

"Well, then," said Eva brightly. "Perhaps you have some questions for me. Perhaps you'd like to ask me about the commonwealth? Perhaps you'd like to know where our colonists stand on the subject of corporations? After all, the colony *is* a corporation, albeit not a greedy unsympathetic one, like some."

Mather looked about the dock restlessly. The native child, whom he now presumed to be a boy, was still standing nearby, staring at him.

"Do they serve whiskey at this colony of yours?"

"Buttermilk, perhaps. And eggnog is not out of the question. In any event, I assure you our hotel is superior to anything you'll find here in town."

"Ah, well, I'm afraid we've already made arrangements in town."

"Well, should you find them lacking anything in the way of refinement, please call on us, Mr. Mather—that is, call on me. The colony is scarcely a mile from town. We have a theater, you know? And razors."

"A theater. Is that so?"

"There's a vaudeville running this week that is positively scandalous from all reports."

"Scandalous, you say?" Rarely had Mather experienced a woman so forward and undaunted.

"Perhaps we'll see you there, Mr. Mather. Good day." Without further ceremony, Eva turned on her heels.

Mather watched her backside as she went. She walked with conviction but also with grace, soft steps and undulating hips. After a half-dozen steps, she turned.

"Mine is the door with the wreath," she called over her shoulder.

Soon she was swallowed up by the crowd. Turning to resume his duties, Mather's eyes landed once more on the native boy, who was presently tilting his head sideways as he continued to stare at Mather. Something was amiss with the child; his spastic movements, his broad forehead, his apparent lack of self-awareness. The boy was an imbecile. Smiling uneasily, Mather resumed his work.

What the Olympic Hotel, with its splintered beams and crooked eaves and buckled floors, lacked in refinement, it offered in proximity to the Belvedere just across the muddy way. The Belvedere, for its part, lacked all refinement but offered whiskey in excess, and a venue to conduct interviews. In spite of its high ceilings—the flimsy construction of which did not inspire confidence—the Belvedere was choked with tobacco smoke. The establishment was a hive of activity and chatter when the party arrived in late afternoon. Perhaps a hundred men, more than half of them standing, crowded the bar. An inventory of their hats alone spoke of the Belvedere's clientele; top hats and coke hats and westerns and cattlemans, homburgs and Dakotas and Sinaloas. Wide-brimmed and narrow-brimmed, tall and squat; of felt and leather and Italian straw. Mather even spotted a lone cavalry hat in their midst. The men beneath them were every bit as dynamic as their haberdashery; clean-faced and stubbled and mustachioed, lean and wide, tall and short, stooping and straight. But every one of them—big or small, wealthy or impoverished—shared an appetite for new possibilities. The same spirit that drew them each to Port Bonita in the first place accounted, too, for the palpable air of excitement in the Belvedere, as Mather and his men made their entrance.

In his station behind the bar, John Tobin, the Belvedere Man, smiled at his own good fortune. At the behest of said proprietor, a line of stools was vacated. All eyes were on Mather and his men as they approached the bar.

"We've been expecting you," said Tobin.

"I can only hope we don't disappoint," Mather said, claiming a stool.

"All around?" said Tobin.

"The house," said Mather gesturing grandly.

When Haywood cocked a dubious brow, Mather patted him firmly on the back. "Not to worry, Charlie. You can thank the *Press*."

Following a round of whiskeys which took nearly a quarter of an hour to procure, Mather and his men, aided by a handful of volunteers, shuffled several tables about, fashioning a makeshift interview station in the far corner of the bar, where a crush of men began to form. The din of the bar soon proved to be to a distraction, so for a small price, Tobin was persuaded to grant Mather use of one of the upstairs rooms, normally reserved for the carnal pursuits of his patrons.

A tired mattress was condemned to a corner, and a desk was moved in from the office. A line of men soon formed up the stairs. For the remainder of the afternoon and deep into the evening, Mather and Haywood conducted interviews.

Tobin himself was among the first to volunteer.

"Whatever you find beyond those mountains, I hope it ain't more Indians."

"Not likely," said Mather.

"Not likely at all," Haywood concurred.

As the evening progressed, no less than two dozen young men pleaded their cases to join the expedition. They hailed from Pennsylvania and Nebraska and Indiana and Ohio; tradesmen, cattlemen, and miners, and even an out-of-work dentist with three fingers on his right hand. Too, there were men who were born and raised in Port Bonita, and New Dungeness, men who'd spent there lives hunting and trapping and logging the hill country from the Elwha to the Hoh. Some of them purported to possess firsthand knowledge of the interior, though invariably upon further inquiry revealed themselves to be ignorant of the mountainous terrain that lay beyond the foothills.

And not all of the men were young. A trapper by the name of Lofall, a West Virginian by way of Missouri, the owner of a dilapidated set of teeth and a gray beard of remarkable proportions, bigger in fact than Mather's, claimed to have navigated the Elwha to its point of origin. When pressed for further information, however, Lofall professed to know the circuitous route to the origin of every river and the least resistant path over every range. It was Lofall who would eventually convince Mather that the Elwha was navigable by flatboat, a conviction that would greatly alter the course of the expedition. For all his enthusiasm, the trapper could not, however, allay Mather's incredulity upon hearing his tallest tale of all.

"When I come out onto the bank—like I say, the river is running low and she ain't too wide, it being late summer—I see it there on the other side, howling like the devil himself. Holding two big river rocks and crashing them together like cymbals. At first I figure it for a bear, standing on its hind legs. But I'm telling you, this was no bear. Didn't howl like any bear, that's a fact. And it didn't have a face like no bear. This was half a bear and half a man, God as my witness."

"Were you armed?" inquired Haywood.

"Yes, I was. And, to be truthful, I can't say why I didn't go for my rifle. I suppose because . . . well, to be perfectly honest, I was scared stiff. Didn't know what exactly I'd be shootin' at."

Later, Mather and Haywood would question the Indians about Lofall's alleged bear-man, and the Indians invariably smiled knowingly but claimed to know nothing. The Klallam, he learned, were a tribe at odds, having splintered in two tribes, neither of which were to be trusted. The Siwash Klallam, wintering at Hollywood Beach, were said to be drunk and unreliable for the most part, while the Klallam at Jamestown, some twenty miles east along the strait, were said to be religious zealots, blinded by temperance and a hatred for whites. Mather opted to question the Siwash Klallam because of their proximity. Their camp was strung out for a half mile or more along the strait east of the harbor, comprising a loosely knit webwork of sagging tents, lean-tos, and odd ménages of shake and tin and canvas that defied classification. Among these habitations, a number of wooden frames had been constructed, festooned with laundry and cured fish carcasses. The gravel shoreline was littered with canoes, heaping from bow to stern with all manner of worldly possessions, from nets to baskets to iron skillets. Fires burned, or rather smoked, in uneven intervals up and down the beach, around which old Klallam women hunched to no purpose, and an occasional drunk was sprawled out.

Mather found the Indians to be every bit as forthcoming, if no more helpful, than the whites. An old woman wrapped in at least four shawls told Mather of a central basin awaiting them beyond the divide, surrounding a vast alpine lake, into whose chill waters all rivers flowed, an idyllic portrait soon corroborated by a half-dozen Klallam. They told of a wide fertile valley brimming yellow with mountain lilies. A land teeming year-round with elk, deer, and all manner of game. However, it was also noted upon nearly every occasion that the natives dared not venture into this paradise. Most were wary to even speak of the reason why. A Klallam elder calling himself Indian George was finally persuaded to explain the matter of a certain fire-spewing bird god who nested there.

"Many years ago, too many to count, the hungry Siwash sent a hunting party deep into the mountains in search of ranging elk," the old man explained. "The hunting was good there. The elk were plenty and offered themselves to the hunters, who were very grateful. But when Thunderbird discovered that the Siwash had entered his home, he grew angry, and he descended screeching from his snowy perch, and swooped down on them, and the beating of his wings uprooted whole forests in front of him. And when he arrived with his deafening caw, the earth heaved. He opened great chasms in the earth, which swallowed the hunters. And Thunderbird dumped mountains and rivers upon the Siwash. And they did not die courageously, our hunters, but begging for their lives. Only a few managed to survive the wrath of Thunderbird, and this they did not manage on their own—they were spared by Thunderbird as messengers to warn the Siwash."

Apparently, the message was still alive and well in 1889, though Mather paid no heed to this warning, nor the bulk of the information he collected at Hollywood Beach, reasoning that the natives were dangerously susceptible to parable and could not be trusted to provide any credible information about the lay of the interior. Mather did, however, find their stories entertaining and judged the Klallam at Hollywood Beach to be in every way superior to the Crees and half-breeds he fought in Manitoba.

After two days of inquiries, the party found their guide in the person of a twenty-eight-year-old Klallam named Abraham Lincoln Charles. Charles was said by a number of his people to be an excellent hunter, fisherman, and tracker, with an impressive knowledge of the Elwha and the surrounding valleys.

It was observed by one elderly Klallam, that Abe Charles was "the best hunter of all the Siwash" and that he never got lost, not even in the driving snow.

"Even if he doesn't know where he is, he knows where to go. The Little Earths live inside his head."

The young Klallam struck an impressive figure. At six foot three, he was nearly Mather's height but leaner and harder. He wore a Mackinaw jacket of Yukon wool and cut his hair short like a white man. Abe Charles was soft-spoken and measured in his delivery, two qualities that never failed to engender confidence in Mather, probably, he was willing to admit, owing to his own vociferous and impulsive manner. Moreover, Abe Charles did not drink. The young Klallam promised to be a welcome addition to the expedition.

Upon the eve of the party's initial push into the interior, however, Abraham Lincoln Charles would stealthily pack his bag by the light of the dying fire and steal quietly downriver into the night.

Editor's note: This excerpt of the novel West of Here *begins the story of settlers on Washington's rugged coast and the natives they enlist to aid in their exploration.*

Copyright by Jonathan Evison, from West of Here *(Algonquin Books, 2011)*

JEAN IYISABWA is from Tanzania. He is sixteen and goes to Arts and Academics Academy in Highline. He wrote this essay in Ms. Reynold's ELL class. One of his best memories is the day he started going to English classes in Tanzania. In the future, he will work as a financial manager.

CHANGING EVERY DAY: THE BILINGUAL EXPERIENCE

Learning a new language wasn't so hard. After all, when I came to the U.S.A. I was already multilingual. English was my fourth language.

Being bilingual can be very helpful when you move to a new country. I was born in Tanzania; that's where I learned Swahili. My parents are from Burundi; that's where I learned Kirundi. Some people in my neighborhood when I was growing up were from Rwanda, and that's where I learned Kinyarwanda. Gaining friends, helping others, and getting new opportunities in life are doors that are opened once you speak more than one language.

When you enter a new country, the first thing to do is to gain friends. It's easier for those who are bilingual. When you are bilingual, you get to meet new people from other countries. In my English class there are students with four different native languages, but we all speak English. This helps a lot because it connects me with people who speak other languages and it makes me feel more included in the class, country, and culture. Gaining friends can also lead to a deep relationship in the future, such as getting married and making a family. When you are bilingual you can make deep connections with people from different backgrounds, which can lead to a new mixed culture. A new person can have a big impact by helping you get to know people who speak different languages. When I first came here, my friend Jean Marie, who also spoke Kirundi, invited me in and helped me meet new people. It helped me learn English quickly because I had friends who spoke English very well. It made me feel more comfortable in my new life. Once you are bilingual and have friends, your life becomes easier in a new country.

Being bilingual is helpful to you but it also lets you help others. Speaking other people's native languages can help them feel more invited. When you are with a person that speaks the same language as you do, it brings you more comfort and confidence and even makes you feel safer. As a bilingual person, you can always help others learn English outside of school. I teach parents sometimes who don't speak English. This makes me feel valuable, that I'm worth something and that I'm important somehow. Being bilingual, I can help others a lot, by translating, helping at school with a new student from another country, and helping my parents with letters at home. When I'm helping others, it makes me feel smart and responsible. I also feel trusted because what I translate can be private sometimes, like when it's from the bank or the doctor. Once you are bilingual in a new a country, you can be very helpful to others in many different ways.

When you are bilingual, opportunities in life just become more open and make your life easier. When it comes to opportunities in life, the first thing to worry about is education. Once you are educated everything else just follows. I want to get an education first before I do anything else. As a new person in the U.S.A., you have to learn English and at least one more language to go to college. Later on in life, I want to become a financial manager. Education is important to me because it's the whole reason my parents came here. They want to see me and my siblings have success in life. Also, once you are bilingual more jobs and careers are open to you and communicating between people becomes easier. When you speak more than one language at work, you feel more helpful than monolingual people, because they have to call up a translator when it comes to working with people who don't speak English. Finally, being bilingual makes traveling much easier and fun. My home languages open a lot of doors for me to travel because there are at least five countries that speak my home languages: Congo, Rwanda, Burundi, Tanzania, and Kenya. Knowing languages can help me gain friends and feel comfortable in a new country quickly. Having people that know you well in a different country is very helpful because you might need them someday. Once you are bilingual, traveling is never a problem.

Learning a new language changes you forever; it helps you gain friends, help others, and get new opportunities in life. Being bilingual has changed my life because I have met people in Seattle from other countries who speak my language, and they have done what they can to help my family. Language connects you with different people and helps you have success in life. In twenty-five years, I picture a world where everybody speaks more than one language. As for me, that world is already here.

Photo by Dan Busta

DAVY ROTHBART is the creator of *Found Magazine*, a frequent contributor to public radio's This American Life, and author of the story collection *The Lone Surfer of Montana, Kansas*. He writes regularly for *GQ, Grantland* and *The Believer*, and his work has also been featured in *The New Yorker, The New York Times*, and *The Sun*. He's lived in Ann Arbor, Michigan for 5/6 of his life.

LIE BIG

One time Mitey-Mike tripped a silent alarm in a jewelry store. It was three-thirty in the morning. The cops came.

He told me about this the next day.

Mitey-Mike saw the cops at the front window. He didn't try to run or hide. He walked right up to them. "Hey!" he shouted through the glass. "You have to go around back. Through the alley. The back door. I don't have the key to this one." He met them at the back door—the door he'd jimmied—and invited them in. "I'll get some coffee going," he said. "Caf or decaf?"

The cops wanted to know who he was. There were four of them. They said they were responding to an alarm.

"I'm Jerry's nephew," Mitey-Mike told them. "Come on in. Give your-selves a break. We've got chairs in here. There's coffee if you want it. I'm going to have a coffee. Actually, I'm going to have a beer. There's beer in the basement. Here, let me get some lights on."

He roamed around the store looking for the light switches. Three of the cops sat down in chairs; the fourth remained standing and watched him. Mitey-Mike found the lights. He turned them on. He walked back over to the cops. "Listen here," he said to the cop who was standing, "have a seat. *Mi casa, su casa.*" He brought a chair over. These were the chairs cus-tomers sat in to peer into the jewelry cases and try on rings and bracelets and talk to the jewelers. It was that kind of store. The cop finally sat down. "Now what can I get for you guys?" said Mitey-Mike. "How 'bout a beer?"

One of the cops said, "We'd like to see some ID, please."

Mitey-Mike stared at him, then stared at each of them, and laughed. "You mean Jerry didn't tell you about the boat?" He paused. He looked them in the eyes. "The boat. You know about the boat, right?" He laughed again. "You guys don't know about the boat. You probably have no idea why I'm here."

He pulled up a chair for himself. "This was the big weekend," he said. "Jerry decided it was time. Well, goddamn, he's been dating the girl the better part of three years. It was more than time. You know her? Nika? The surgeon? No? Okay. Anyway, he took her up to Drummond Island for the weekend. He's got the place there. The beach house. Comfy, but there's spiders. He got me to come along. Anne, too. He wanted us to videotape it when he popped the question. The idea was, we'll have the camera out and be messing with it. On the beach. Filming the sunset. Then he'll get down on one knee."

The cops looked on with a mixture of bafflement, boredom, and lingering suspicion.

"The ring," Mitey-Mike continued. "Now Jerry's got some nice rings right here in the shop. In fact, if you'd like, you're welcome to try some on. Look around. Let me know what catches your eye. But the point is, Nika used to work here. Before med school. She knows the goddamn inventory. Jerry's not going to just pluck something out of the case. It's got to be special. It was special. Listen.

"They went to Morocco in February. Sure, just leave me here alone, Jerry, leave me here all alone to run things during Valentine's Day rush. Thanks a lot, Jerry. So. They're in Marrakech. The marketplace. Crazy narrow streets. Thousands of twists and turns. I saw pictures. Well, what happens is, they get separated from each other in there. Jerry's not worried —Nika's a big girl, she can take care of herself, she can find her way back to the hotel. This is perfect, though. Jerry can look for a ring in secret. He finds this old-man jeweler, a nomad—they call them Blue Men—they're tribal peoples, desert folk. This old guy makes these rings, okay? You know what a quarter-cusp is?" Mitey-Mike leaned in toward the cop nearest him. "Here, let me see your hand."

"We can't stay long," said the cop. His walkie-talkie buzzed with radio traffic.

"Okay. Fast forward, fast forward. Listen," said Mitey-Mike, "Jerry's all ready to give her the ring. This was the big weekend. But this morning we go out to the boat, me and Jerry, and yeah, you guessed it. *The boat fucking flips*. Now this is the weird part. We'd hit something underwater. That's what flipped us. But guess what it was. I'll tell you. It was a *car*, an *automobile*—for example, what you'd drive to the market in or pile full of kids for their Saturday morning soccer game. We hit a car with his boat. Jerry had the ring in his coat pocket. Well, that's gone. My wallet's gone, too, but that stuff's easy to replace."

The cop who was last to sit down now stood. "What'd he do," the cop chuckled, "send you all the way back down here to get another ring?"

"Yes, sir. And his scuba gear."

The cop looked at him. "I thought the guy who owned this place was named Maynard."

"Maynard?" said Mitey-Mike. "Maynard's just the manager. He's a moron. No, he's a nice guy. But he's terrible with the books. You know what, though. He saved Jerry's life once." He raised his eyebrows. "Australia. Sharks."

At this point, in recounting the story to me, Mitey-Mike fell silent. We were shooting baskets at Wheeler Park, down by the old train station. "Well, what happened?" I asked him.

"What do you mean?"

"What do you mean, 'what do you mean?' What happened next?"

"Nothing. They left. I told them I'd close up. I told them to stop by during business hours and take a look at our fine selection." Mitey-Mike reached into his jeans with both hands and pulled a long gold chain from each pocket. "Here," he said. "Take your pick."

I looked at him.

"There's a lesson in this," he said.

"What's that?"

He bounced the basketball and shot from thirty feet, an airball that rolled all the way into the grass. "*Swish!*" he said. He grinned at me. "Lie big."

Mitey-Mike always lied big. He told marvelous lies, outlandish lies, terrible and astounding lies, sad and dangerous lies, silly lies, beautiful, exquisite and thunderous lies. He lied, mostly, to get out of trouble, but often he lied for no reason at all. Times when truth would have sufficed, when a small lie would have done the job, he still lied big. Preposterous lies, he said, had more style. He lied to teachers and cops, to employers, to girlfriends, and even to me, his best friend. Once, twenty minutes late to pick me up at Bell's Pizza, where we both worked, he arrived with a story of taking his cousin's ferret on an emergency trip to the vet.

"Look, don't worry about it," I said.

"I *am* worried," he said. "I'm worried about little Smokey. I don't know if the poor rascal's gonna make it through the night. They think he was poisoned. What kind of creep would poison a little kid's ferret?"

Nothing was too sacred to use for material. In high school, I'd heard him explain to a math teacher after class why he hadn't brought his homework in. His brother in Rhode Island, Mitey-Mike said, had called him the night before, suicidal. Mitey-Mike spoke very softly and slowly and stared at his hands. "I could hear that his voice was funny," he said. "Not funny like upset, just weird-sounding, and I asked him why, and he told me, well, the gun was in his mouth."

Mitey-Mike sometimes said that as an authority on lying it was important to pass his knowledge onto others, and by others he meant me. He said that the best lies didn't have to make sense and didn't have to relate directly to what you were lying about—if something disastrous had really happened to you, it's unlikely you'd be able to explain yourself clearly. One of his favorite strategies was to appear badly shaken and cry out in deep inexpressible sorrow, "The *dogs*. They were shitting *everywhere*. They just kept shitting and shitting!" He believed there were other can't-miss lines, like any that involved spilling a steaming-hot drink into your own lap and burning your penis. No one in history had ever been asked to supply a doctor's note for a burnt penis.

Mitey-Mike always cautioned me not to say too much, not to over-explain. People who are telling the truth, he said, never feel the need to go into too much detail, though there were also times, he acknowledged, when an incredible story was necessary, like when he'd been caught inside the jewelry store.

Never back down from a lie, Mitey-Mike instructed me.

Whenever someone challenged him, he'd respond with wounded ferocity, with such blazing and forceful conviction that people either believed him or gave into the lie rather than continue the argument. He was a bully in that way. On the basketball court, if his team scored the first point of the game, he'd call out the score, "Four-nothing."

Someone on the other team would protest. "Four? That's the first bucket."

Mitey-Mike's eyes would go wide and he'd howl, "No fucking *way*! I scored twice myself,"—he'd point at me—"and my man right here scored one. That's three-nothing. Check it up."

Sometimes the lies turned ugly. Mitey-Mike lied to his girlfriends. He usually had two or three girlfriends at the same time. I saw the hurt in their faces when he lied to them—they knew he was lying but pretended to themselves and to him that they didn't. Mitey-Mike found ways to make me complicit in his lies. He'd leave one girl's house and pick me up at my grandma's, and together we'd drive over to another one of his girlfriend's houses. She'd be upset that he was an hour and a half late, and he'd explain that we'd been giving my grandma a bath. The girl would look at me and I'd nod gravely and explain, "She gets sores if we don't get her out of bed and into the tub every few days." Then Mitey-Mike would drop me off back at my house and speed away with the girl.

You might think I'd get tired of all the lies but I never did. Each sad and damaging lie he told was followed by thirty wild, joyous, sprawling, magical lies. It was a glorious feeling to be in cahoots with him, to be backstage, behind the curtain, on the side of *knowing*, and watch him weave his brilliant tapestries. People delighted in him and his power over them was mesmerizing.

From fifth grade on, Mitey-Mike was my best friend and really my only friend—when I hung out with other people he got jealous and brooded around town until I abandoned my new friends and came back to him. In me he had a sidekick, someone to witness all of his impossible feats; in turn, he provided me with adventure and a way to meet girls. We were a pretty good team for about fourteen years. But you know how it is. Things fall apart.

First, Katy appeared. She came into Bell's Pizza one night after we'd already closed, a shy, beautiful, pale-skinned girl with green hair, wearing big jeans and a Joe Dumars jersey. I was up front counting out the register; Mitey-Mike was in back mopping out the walk-in cooler—if we'd been reversed, things might have unfolded differently. I gave Katy two free slices of pizza and asked for her phone number; within a couple of weeks we were a couple.

My love for Katy was sharp and aching. When she wasn't right next to me I was miserable. Even when we were lying close together or, you know, making with the love, I still couldn't seem to get close enough. I'd always imagined that Mitey-Mike would disapprove when I finally found a girl to be with because I'd be less available to him, but he was cool about Katy. He said it made him feel good to see me so wrapped up in someone. He seemed genuinely happy for me. A couple of weekends in a row he covered my shifts so Katy and I could go camping up north.

One night in August I got off work early, before midnight, and went looking for Mitey-Mike to see if he wanted to play some basketball. Through the front window of his house, in the glow from the TV, I saw him making out with a girl on the living room floor. I'd actually happened upon this type of scene at his house a couple of time before and had jetted, but this time I stayed for a moment because the Tigers game was on the TV and I could see that Detroit had runners at second and third with nobody out. I must have gotten caught up in the game because a couple of minutes later I realized all of a sudden that Mitey-Mike and the girl were sitting up and staring at me. You know how you can look at something and not really see it for what it is, and then there's this tremor and things flip into place? For about a second and, oh, maybe another third of a second, it was just Mitey-Mike and a girl—then things popped into focus, and it was Mitey-Mike and Katy.

A great, deafening, roaring sound filled my ears; blood banged its way through my neck and my arms; my entire body buzzed like I'd grabbed hold of a downed power line. The world came to me in a series of fade-ins and fade-outs. I remember running as hard as I could, chased by Mitey-Mike. The next thing I knew I was sitting on the front porch of a house somewhere, Mitey-Mike standing over me, his face a foot away. I was yelling at him and he was yelling back. At some point the porch light turned on and an old man appeared in the doorway. "The fuck you looking at!" Mitey-Mike screamed at the guy. Next we were running again, all the way through downtown, and then we were standing on the basketball court at Wheeler Park, heaving for breath and drenched in sweat.

Mitey-Mike shook me by the shoulders. "Look at me," he said. "Look at me!

You think you know what you saw—but you don't! You don't!"

I pushed away from him and screeched for him to fuck off.

He shook me again. "You need to chill the fuck out! I was giving her a back rub! Do you understand? A silly fucking back rub!"

Maybe I was crying, I don't know. I sagged away. "Can you tell me the truth," I said. My head pounded. "It's me, okay? Come on, now. It's me. Just tell me what's happening. I just want to know what's happening."

"Nothing's happening," he said. "We're here at the park. We're talking. Katy's probably wondering where the hell we are."

I tore at my forehead and cheeks. "Mike, I saw, okay?" I saw it all. You don't have to make anything up. I saw what I saw. I saw you guys."

Mitey-Mike was quiet for a bit. The night pulsed. Finally he said, "Okay, listen. You want to hear everything, I'll tell you. I asked Katy to come over for a reason. I askéd her to bring me something specific over, some medicine, some hydrocortisone cream. Listen to me! She was helping me put it on. Earlier today—listen to me! Earlier today, I spilled bleach on myself. Listen! I burnt my penis."

Memory is strange. I don't remember punching him, I just remember him saying that last thing, then looking up at me with his face covered in blood. "You're bleeding," I said, surprised by it. Then I turned and ran.

For about six months my dad had been in my ear, asking me to come out to Sacramento and help him with his business. He sold trampolines to rich people. A week later I was out there learning the ropes.

In late December, two days before the new year, Mitey-Mike was killed in an accident. It was the kind of spectacular tale he might have come up with himself after missing a week of work. What happened was he was walking his neighbor's dog in a field near his house and he got hit by an airplane. A little two-man Cessna. Both pilots died and so did Mitey-Mike, but the dog lived. Hassan, my old boss at Bell's Pizza, explained everything. I'd never heard him so upset. "Will you come back for the funeral?" he asked me. I told him I didn't know.

Katy called the next day, New Year's Eve. She was crying. We talked for a long time. She told me she'd loved Mitey-Mike; I told her I'd loved him too. She said they'd found an apartment together in Ypsilanti and they were supposed to move in on the first day of February. They'd bought some furnishings already—drapes and a furry toilet-seat cover.

"What are you gonna do?" I asked her.

"I don't know," she said. "I was thinking of moving out there to California."

"Here?"

"Well, to L.A. You remember Jenna? She lives there."

"It'd be nice to have you out here. L.A.'s not too far from here."

"Yeah. That would be nice." She began to cry again.

"You know what I'm wearing," I said. "I'm wearing that gold necklace he gave me. Remember that long gold chain he gave me? From when he broke into that jewelry store? He had one that matched it. Remember?"

Katy said, "I know which one you're talking about."

"Yeah, I wear it every day. I guess I have since he gave it to me." I wrapped the long end of it around my fingers and through them. "Katy, you know that jewelry store story, right? How he broke in and there was a silent alarm and the cops came?"

"I know that story," she said. "That's your favorite Mitey-Mike story. You love that story. You always tell that story. You told me that story before I even met him."

"Yeah, it's a good story."

"Well, he made it up. Last week he told me. No, two weeks ago. He got that necklace at Bunky's on Michigan Avenue. His necklace, too, the one that matched. He traded his old Nintendo for them. And a bunch of games." She took a long staggered breath. Someone else was saying something to her in the background. "Listen," she said, "I got to go. Let's talk later. Can we talk some more? Can we talk tomorrow? I think we should keep talking."

My head and my hands felt light. "Call me tomorrow," I said.

"Okay. 'Bye then. Happy New Year's."

"Okay," I said. "Okay. Okay. Happy New Year."

THE IMPORTANCE OF BEING ENVIOUS

Tom Robbins

At the onset, I have to state that I'm not convinced that there's any such thing as "writer's block." I suspect that what we like to call "writer's block" is in fact a failure of nerve or a failure of imagination or both.

If you're willing to break rules, risk ridicule, and explore the unknown, and if you've somehow managed, despite social conditioning, to hold on to your imagination (more's the pity if you haven't), then you can dissolve any so-called block simply by imagining extraordinary, heretofore unthinkable solutions, and/or by playing around uninhibitedly with language. It's quite possible to imagine or wordplay, conjure or sport your way out of any impasse.

Prolonged neurotic blockages aside, however, it would be false not to acknowledge that every working writer experiences days when the ideas and images reveal themselves more reluctantly than usual. Biorhythms could be at fault, it could be a savage hangover, external or internal distractions, or one of those ruptures that occur periodically in the pipeline from the Other. (Writing imaginative fiction is such a mysterious enterprise that often there's no way to explain its sources except to attribute them to Something Out There Somewhere.)

On those dreaded occasions when your muse shambles in wearing army boots, it may be time to tap into one of the strongest and most persistent, if seldom discussed, human emotions: *jealousy.*

Yes, we should never underestimate the valuable role that sheer envy plays in the creative process. Whereas in a romantic relationship jealousy is stupid and destructive, as a lubricant of the verbal brain machinery it can be highly effective. It's elementary: you read a few pages (sometimes a few paragraphs or even a line or two will suffice) of work of which you are in awe, and in minutes you'll find yourself motivated—burning! —to try to compose passages of equal merit.

Well, at least envy can usually motivate *me*. On a pedestrian morning, grounded in a no-fly zone without a banjo on my knee, I'll read, say, a poem by Pablo Neruda or César Vallejo, turn to the early pages of Anaïs Nin's *Seduction of the Minotaur*, sample a bit of Pynchon, Nabokov, or Henry Miller; or even dial up Bob Dylan on the iPod, and soon I've waxed six shades of pistachio and kiwi. The green beast has awakened and is starting to chase me down the street.

Call it forced inspiration if you will, call it literary Viagra, but as a writing exercise, envy works. "Could I not coin phrases that smoke and pop like those do?" I'll ask. "Is that guy's word-bag really that much bigger than mine?" Or, "Do I have the gust to work as close to the bull as she does?" Feeling almost ashamed in the presence of such verve, I'll return to my idling narrative primed to redeem—and entertain—myself.

By no means is this a case of competing for fortune or fame. It isn't as if I want to elbow Salman Rushdie out of line at the bank or steal Louise Erdrich's magical ink. What I desire is to feel for myself the *rush* Salman or Louise must have felt when they pulled that particular rabbit out of a hat. What I covet is to have the kind of effect on language-conscious readers that Rushdie and Erdrich have just had on me.

Ultimately, it doesn't matter whether your prose actually meets the master's unintentional challenge. That degree of success is probably not in your cards. But you have to believe it might be. And in merely attempting, with every muscle in your envious psyche, to climb to that elevation—to be that inventive and amusing and tough and daring and true—you may well have mooned the drab angel of mediocrity, and if nothing else, you will have let loose your juice.

ADDITIONAL CONTRIBUTORS

 **JUSTIN ALLAN** is a long-time 826 Seattle employee. In addition to managing the Greenwood Space Travel Supply Company and designing, he and his partner operate a screen-printing studio, Cellar Door Mercantile, out of their 650 square-foot apartment. See his art in "Snow Perfect" in this book.

 **SKYLAAR AMANN** hand-binds books, draws illustrations and comics, writes poetry, and sews plush sea creatures. She also plays ukulele. The only thing she loves more than the art stuff is the Pacific Ocean and the wonders of the tide line. Skylaar was born in Rochester, New York, and grew up on the Oregon Coast. She currently lives in Portland. See her art in "Two Crimson Beets" in this book.

 **NICK BELARDES** teaches for Memoir Journal, Inc. He founded Random Writers Workshop in 2009, is author of "Lords," (2004), "Random Obsessions" (2009), "Small Places" (the first Twitter novel on the planet [2008]), and "Songs of the Glue Machines" (2013). See his art in "West of Here" in this book.

ADDITIONAL CONTRIBUTORS

SARA EWALT started Pinyadayada after an afternoon trip to the Georgetown Trailer Park Mall in Seattle. One of the Airstreams was dressed up as a piñata. An idea was born! That weekend, the first pinyada was made. When not under a pile of tissue paper, Sara can be found in Seattle adventuring in the woods, enjoying a happy hour with friends, canning seasonal goodness and tracking down good times. See her art in "How to Fall" in this book.

Photo by Harley Soltes

KÄREN JURGENSEN grew up in rural Republic, Washington, where her grandmother took her on her first foraging adventures. In addition to her work at the Quillisascut Farm School of the Domestic Arts, Kären is a chef instructor at the Seattle Culinary Academy, a mercenary cook, and a restaurant consultant in Seattle. She founded the Seattle chapter of Chefs Collaborative. See her recipe in "Winter Dreaming" in this book.

Photo by Betty Udesen

HARLEY SOLTES is an award-winning photographer who was on staff at the Seattle Times for twenty-two years, working on an array of international, domestic, and regional photo assignments. A freelancer since 2005, he has photographed stories for LIFE, Sports Illustrated, TIME, People, and the National Geographic Society. He continues his work as a photojournalist while running a farm in Kingston, Washington. See his photographs in "Winter Dreaming" in this book.

ACKNOWLEDGEMENTS

This is our third edition of *What to Read in the Rain* and, like the first two editions, it is the product of hard work by many people. They include:

THE PRODUCTION TEAM
who pulls the book together, meets with hotel general managers, organizes copyeditors, asks authors, manages authors, fulfills book orders, drives the books to the hotels, and generally sits around and has big ideas:

Justin Allan, Deb Clothier, Alicia Craven, Teri Hein, Margot Kenly, Samantha Redsell, and Bill Thorness

THE ADULT AUTHORS
who donated their work for this edition. Some wrote new work especially for this book while others generously allowed us to reprint previously published works:

Shannon Borg, Arthur Bradford, Chelsea Cain, Langdon Cook, William Dietrich, Dave Eggers, Jonathan Evison, Kathleen Flenniken, David Lasky, Jared Leising, Lora Lee Misterly, Peter Mountford, Naseem Rakha, Nancy Rawles, Peter Rock, Tom Robbins, Davy Rothbart, and Harold Taw

THE STUDENT AUTHORS
who labored over their stories in 826 Seattle workshops throughout the year:

Eli Arao, Edom Araya, Musaab Bargicho, Edith Martinez Bringas, Lucille Corbit, Ny'il Damis-Salaam, Nathanael Daniel, Nazrawit Dessie, Melat Ermyas, Barbie Ferrer, Stella Frechette, Yonase Geleta, Ava Hall, Gabe Honeycutt, Jean Iyisabwa, Sada Kalbach, Lucia Minahan, Rowan Murray, Cece Rosenman, Kiera Rudden-Flanagan, Kathleen Santarelli, Jasmine Sun, Esa Tilija, Kim Vo, Rachel Witus, Mimi Zekaryas, and Aaron Zekaryas

ACKNOWLEDGEMENTS

OUR YOUTH ADVISORY BOARD MEMBERS WHO SERVED ON OUR EDITORIAL ADVISORY BOARD:
Isbah Barlas, Lucille Corbit, Justin Ith, Meron Kesahun, Carter Sherman, Mahie Solomon, Rachel Whitus, and Sam Zagula

THE WORKSHOP TEACHERS, THEIR ASSISTANTS, 826 SEATTLE CLASSROOM TUTORS AND 826 SEATTLE ADULT EDITORIAL ADVISORY BOARD MEMBERS:
Kit Bakke, David Blinn, Natalie Champ, Daryle Conners, Lauren Davenport, Sarah Delaney, Angela J. Fountas, Stephanie Forman, Megan Kelso, Khristina Kravas, Emily Knudsen, Susan Kostick, Annie Kuo, Julia Littlefield, Jake Lindsay, Tony Monda, Angela Peck, Claudia Rowe, Ann Senechal, Brad Shigenaka, Jennie Shortridge, and Tamara Vallejos

Special thanks to all of the talented people who support the creation of all the youth writing work at 826 Seattle. We could not possibly include the names of all these people.

IN-SCHOOL PROGRAM TEACHERS:
Natalie Coots, Sara Esrick, Carla Reynolds, and James Jarosz

THE BOOK DESIGNER, WHOSE MANY HOURS OF DONATED WORK PRODUCED THIS BEAUTIFUL BOOK:
Tony Ong

EDITOR AND PROJECT MANAGER EXTRAORDINAIRE:
Bill Thorness

COPYEDITOR:
Angela Jane Fountas

ACKNOWLEDGEMENTS

826 SEATTLE STAFF, AN EXTRAORDINARY GROUP OF VERY HARDWORKING PEOPLE:

Justin Allan, Alex Allred, Humaira Barlas, Isbah Barlas, Alicia Craven, Michelle DeBruyn, Teri Hein, Peggy Allen Jackson, Leslie McCallum, May Nguyen, Samantha Redsell, Sue Spang, and Steve Yasakawa

SUPPORTERS WHO HELPED FUND THE PUBLICATION OF THIS BOOK:

Sappi Fine Paper Company

Amazon.com

THE HOTELS IN SEATTLE

who are partnering with us to offer this book to their guests. Special thanks to the people of those hotels who believed (and rightly so) that a book so intrinsically local, written by children and adults, would enhance their guests' stays. Our hotel partners:

Ace Hotel

Alexis Hotel

Cedarbrook Lodge

Grand Hyatt Seattle

Hilton Seattle

Hyatt at Olive 8

Inn at the WAC

Renaissance Seattle Hotel

DON'T FORGET TO WRITE!

Want to be in next year's book? Drop us a postcard!

Here's what two of our intrepid reader-travelers sent us this year:

An April visit. Seattle was "mudlucious," green and clean, scoured by wind and rain. We rode the #12 bus, up and down, leaning, careening, nearly falling. Back at the hotel, we discovered "Monster" by Karen Finneyfrock (wow). Read aloud with appropriate drama. Bought that book real quick.

—CHERIE, SANTA BARBARA

Discovered the anthology during our first night at the Renaissance. I wanted to take a copy with me, mostly for Tom Robbins' Advice to Aspiring Writers! That book was my late night companion throughout our journey. I loved reading it at Sooke-Harbor House while listening to the waves lapping the shore and the crackle of the dying embers! Kudos to you for such a great initiative!

—ELLEN, NEW YORK CITY

Send us a postcard with your story.
- Make it 50 words or so (plus your contact info)
- We will convene a panel of our most creative writers to review all entries
- The best entries will be published in next year's edition

(The fine print: Sending your entry constitutes your permission for us to edit and publish your work.)

Send your postcard to:
826 Seattle
Attn: Intrepid Traveler Desk
PO Box 30764
Seattle, WA 98113